GENERAL BIOLOGY
A Human Orientation

Second Edition

Lea K. Bleyman
Emil Gernert Jr.
John M. Utting
Morris Winokur

City University of New York
Bernard Baruch College
New York, New York

PEARSON

Custom
Publishing

Printed in the United States of America

20 19 18 17 16 15 14

Please visit our web site at www.pearsoncustom.com

ISBN 0–536–63362–2

PEARSON CUSTOM PUBLISHING
75 Arlington Street, Suite 300, Boston, MA 02116
A Pearson Education Company

Preface

This laboratory manual is designed for a one semester course in Introductory Biology, primarily for non-science majors. Our aim is to introduce biological principles by the "hands-on" approach whenever possible. Thus, students are required to observe, dissect and experiment where appropriate to the exercise. The focus of the course is the relation of the structure of biological systems to their function with, whenever possible, emphasis on humans.

Acknowledgments

Many helpful suggestions were made by the Biology Staff of the Department of Natural Sciences of Baruch Collge of The City University of New York. A special mention of thanks is due Dr. R. M. Bradley who reviewed the manuscript, as well as an especially heartfelt appreciation to Mrs. Lucy Krishok for her exemplary secretarial services.

TABLE OF CONTENTS

1
MEASUREMENT

Science is defined in Webster's New World Dictionary as the "systematized knowledge of nature and the physical world". This systematized knowledge is derived from observations, hypotheses and universal experimentation. These result in the establishment of scientific truth: a theory. The steps used to derive a theory are inherent in all empirical (experimental) sciences and are referred to as the scientific method. Biology, the study of living things, is an empirical science, an experimental science. When confronted with the unknown or a problem to be solved, the biologist, as an empirical scientist, relies on the scientific method. In order to arrive at a theory by way of the scientific method, the observations of the scientist in solving various problems are key elements in establishing a testable hypothesis, a statement based on observations. Remember that a hypothesis is not accepted as true (a theory) until tested with controlled experimentation, repeated universally. The observations made by the scientist are qualitative (expressed in descriptive terms) and quantitative (expressed in numerical terms). For example, if a car speeds by you, you can say that the car was going very fast. This is a qualitative observation. The policeman at the corner writing a speeding ticket for the driver notes that the car was traveling 60 miles per hour in a 30 miles per hour speed zone! This is a quantitative observation. In science, quantitative observations are measured exclusively with the metric system, and not the English system which is utilized almost exclusively (except for liter bottles of liquids) for quantitative measurements in the United States. The most common parameters that will be mentioned or discussed in your studies in the sciences include length, volume, mass and temperature. The beauty of the metric system lay in the fact that quantitative descriptions are in powers of ten. Certain prefixes describe the metric quantities being considered.

TABLE 1-1 PREFIXES FOR METRIC SYSTEM

PREFIX	ABBREVIATION	QUANTITATIVE DESCRIPTION
kilo	k	$1000 = 10^3$
deci	d	$0.1 = 10^{-1}$
centi	c	$0.01 = 10^{-2}$
milli	m	$0.001 = 10^{-3}$
micro	μ	$0.000001 = 10^{-6}$
nano	n	$0.000000001 = 10^{-9}$
pico	p	$0.000000000001 = 10^{-12}$

The first metric unit to be considered is **volume**, the space occupied by an object. The basic unit is the **liter** (L). From Table 1-1, it can be determined that a deciliter (dl) is 10^{-1} L, a milliliter (ml) is 10^{-3} L, a microliter μl is 10^{-6} L, etc.

The second metric unit is **length**, the shortest distance between two points. The basic metric unit is the **meter** (m). From Table 1-1, it can be determined that a kilometer (km) is 10^3m, a millimeter (mm) is 10^{-3}m, a micrometer (μ or μm) is 10^{-6}m, etc. In some scientific literature reference will be made to the *Angstrom,* (Å), which is 10^{-10} m.

The third metric unit is **mass**, the quantity of matter in a given object. The basic metric unit is the **gram** (g). A kilogram (kg) is 10^{+3} kg, a milligram (mg) is 10^{-3} g, a microgram (μg) is 10^{-6} g, etc.

Another important parameter employed in science is temperature. Temperature is a measure of the heat of an object. In scientific studies temperature is reported in degrees Celsius (°C), not Fahrenheit with which you are more familiar. To interconvert Fahrenheit and Celsius:

$$°C = 5/9 \ (°F - 32) \qquad °F = 9/5(°C) + 32$$

When measuring the different parameters discussed above, the sensitivity or the limits of resolution of the instrumentation employed is important in determining the significance or degree of accuracy of the measurement. For example, suppose that you are measuring the width of a squirrel molar tooth employing a caliper marked in millimeters. The caliper is accurate to the nearest tenth (0.1) mm. If the caliper reads 3.4 mm, the possible range of diameter for the squirrel tooth is from 3.35 mm to 3.45 mm. The number 3.4 has two **significant figures**. If you add a zero in the hundredths place, 3.40, the meaning is changed to three significant figures and the possible range is from 3.395 mm to 3.405 mm. Recording the measurement as 3.40 is wrong if the accuracy of the caliper is only to tenths of a millimeter.

When data is recorded it may be presented in table or graph form. The presentation must have a title and possibly an explanatory caption. The columns in the table and the axes of a graph must be clearly labeled. The first column of a table or the x-axis (horizontal) of a graph display the **independent variable,** which increases or decreases by arbitrarily determined increments such as time or size ranges. The **dependent variable** is displayed on the y-axis (vertical) and is a function of the independent variable. It could be the number of individuals of a given size range or the size of a population in a given year. The units and dimensions of the variables are always clearly marked along the two axes.

PROBLEMS - CALCULATIONS UTILIZING THE METRIC SYSTEM. (Your instructor will work through these problems with you)

A. **Length**

1. How many cm are there in 1.5 km?

_____

2. How many mm are there in a cm?

_____

3. If there are 2.54 cm/inch. How many μm are there per inch?

_____

4. How tall are you in cm?

_____

B. **Volume**

1. How many ml are there in 1.5 L?

_____

2. How many μl are there in a dl?

_____

C. Mass

1. How many mg are there in 1.5 kg?

_____

2. How many g are there in a. 0.5 kg, and b. 0.5mg?

a. _____

b. _____

D. Temperature

1. What is your body temperature in ºC?

_____

VOLUME MEASUREMENTS

A. Your lab instructor will show you various types of glassware (plasticware) that are used in scientific experiments and their uses.

B. Measure 100 ml of water employing a 100 ml graduated cylinder. Note that the surface of the water does form a straight line, but rather a curved surface. This is referred to as a **meniscus**. The accurate determination of the volume is made by reading the bottom of the curved surface and not the edges which adhere to the sides of the graduated cylinder. Measuring from the sides can result in small yet very significant errors when preparing solutions for experimentation.

C. Measure 100 ml of water into a calibrated beaker. Pour the 100 ml from the beaker into the graduated cylinder. Which is a more accurate method for determining volumes? Now pour the 100 ml from the graduated cylinder into a volumetric flask. Is the meniscus above, below or right on the indicator line etched on the stem of the volumetric flask? Again, which is the more accurate measure of volume?

D. How can you be sure which of the above is the most accurate? (Hint: The density of water is 1 gm/cc. 1 cc = 1 cubic centimeter, which for water is 1 ml. Therefore, each ml of water weighs 1 gram.)

WEIGHT DETERMINATIONS

A. For this part of the experiment a digital balance will be employed which measures weight between 0.1 and 200.0 g. Make sure that the units are set for grams and that the balance is "tared" to zero before measuring the weights of the experimental samples. Your instructor will demonstrate the proper use of the balance.

B. Obtain twenty pine cones and record their individual weights in the following table. Remember the previous discussion on significant figures.

Sample #	Weight g
1	
2	
3	
4	
5	
6	
7	
8	
9	
10	
11	
12	
13	
14	
15	
16	
17	
18	
19	
20	
$\sum$	
MEAN	
MEDIAN	

1. Does every pine cone have the same weight? _____

2. What is the range (lowest and highest) of the pine cone weights? _____

3. Sum the weights of the pine cones and enter in the Table ($\sum$).

4. Calculate the mean or average weight by dividing the sum of the weights by n, the total number of pine cones weighed. Enter this value in the Table. Is the mean weight the same for all of the samples?_____ For any of the samples?_____

5. What is the median weight? The median of the sample is the observation with an equal number of observations above and below it. In samples with an even number of observations, the value half way between the two middle observations is used. Enter this value in the Table. Is the median value the same as the mean.?_____

6. Make a bar graph or histogram of your data and of the class data on the following graph.

C. Obtain twenty broad beans and record their individual weights in the following table.

Sample #	Weight g
1	
2	
3	
4	
5	
6	
7	
8	
9	
10	
11	
12	
13	
14	
15	
16	
17	
18	
19	
20	
Σ	
MEAN	
MEDIAN	

1. Does every broad bean have the same weight? _____

2. What is the range (lowest and highest) of the broad bean weights? _____

3. Sum the weights of the broad beans and enter in the Table (Σ).

4. Calculate the mean or average weight and enter this value in the Table. Is the mean weight the same for all of the samples?_____ For any of the samples?_____

5. Determine the median weight and enter this value in the Table. Is the median value the same as the mean.?_____

6. Place all of the beans that were weighed individually on the balance and weigh them all together. Is the total weight of the beans the same as the sum of the individual weights determined in step 3? _____ Why might there be a difference?_____

_____

7. Calculate the mean weight of a bean by dividing the total weight determined in step 6 by twenty. Is the average determined the same as calculated in step 4 when the beans were weighed individually?_____ How can you account for the possible difference?_____

D. Count out 100 radish seeds into a petri dish.

1. Can you determine the weight of a single radish seed with this balance? Why not?_____

2. What is the total weight of the 100 radish seeds? Determine this by placing a empty petri dish cover (or bottom) on the balance, taring the balance (setting the balance to zero), and placing the 100 radish seed into the petri dish.

3. What is the mean weight of the radish seeds? _____

4. Can the range or median value be determined? _____

Some of the experiments in this exercise were designed by students and faculty of Baruch College for NSF Grant #DUE-9354712.
A special thanks to Drs.Holland and Wahlert for the inclusion of some of their material in this experiment.

2
SIMPLE BIOCHEMISTRY

Living systems as we know them have evolved on planet earth due to the presence of atoms which are bound together by different types of bonds. These bonds can be relatively strong (requiring much energy to break them) such as covalent and ionic bonds, or weak such as hydrogen, Van der Waals, and hydrophobic interactions. In living systems, molecules formed by covalent bonds are composed almost exclusively of six atoms: carbon (C), oxygen (O), hydrogen (H) nitrogen (N), phosphorous (P), and sulphur (S). Most of the molecules which make up living systems are covalent compounds with **carbon backbones**. These are referred to as **organic molecules**. There are four major classes of organic molecules: **carbohydrates** - sugars; **lipids** - fats; **proteins**; and **nucleic acids**.

Carbohydrates - sugars (saccharides) - The main function of carbohydrates in your diet and in living things is a source of energy. Carbohydrates are also involved as recognition factors in many cellular processes such as membrane transport and immune responses. Structurally, sugars are classified as monosaccharides (single sugars), disaccharides (double sugars), oligosaccharides (small chains of sugars), and polysaccharides (long chains of sugars).

Monosaccharides are single sugars which can be trioses - 3 carbon sugars, tetroses - 4 carbon sugar, pentoses - 5 carbon sugar, hexoses - 6 carbon sugar, and sedheptuloses - 7 carbon sugars. Triose, tetrose and sedheptulose sugars will be mentioned in lecture in discussions on intermediary metabolism. Important pentoses in living systems are **ribose** (found in Ribonucleic acid, RNA) and **deoxyribose** (found in deoxyribonucleic acid, DNA). Important hexoses in living systems are **glucose, galactose,** and **fructose**. Glucose is required in your body because the brain requires glucose for energy. Therefore, the plasma glucose concentration is maintained at a constant level of approximately 90mg%, which your body maintains by many different mechanisms. These will be discussed later in the semester.

Disaccharides are composed of two monosaccharides held together by covalent bonds formed by dehydration synthesis (the removal of water) from the two sugars. Important disaccharides include: **sucrose** (table sugar) - composed of glucose & fructose; **lactose** (milk sugar) - composed of glucose & galactose; **maltose** (malt sugar, formed from breakdown of starch and glycogen) composed of glucose & glucose.

Oligosaccharides are intermediate length sugars formed from the breakdown of polysaccharides and are found in small quantities in living systems.

Polysaccharides are long chain molecules - they are **glucose polymers** including: **starch** - a glucose polymer found in **plants** which functions as an energy storage molecule; **glycogen** - a glucose polymer found in **animals** which functions as an energy storage molecule; **cellulose** - a glucose polymer found in **plants** functioning for structural support making up the cell walls of plant cells (these cells make up wood and are used to make paper. In your diet, this is referred to as 'fiber' or 'roughage').

Lipids, the second major class of organic molecules, like carbohydrates, are a significant source of energy in your body. Excess calories in your diet are stored as fat in **adipose** tissue. When plasma glucose levels fall below normal levels, proteins and then fats are converted to glucose. (This is the reason that dieting results in the loss of weight.) Lipids are also important as **insulation and protection** of organs. Lipids make up **hormones**, such as estrogens and androgens. **Vitamins D,A,K,E**, are lipid soluble vitamins. Lipids are a very important part of **cell membranes**. Lipids have two basic structures - **glycerides** and **steroids**. **Glycerides** are made up of fatty acids and glycerol. Fatty acids are chains of carbon atoms joined by covalent bonds. These can either be **saturated** or **unsaturated**. (Structures will be discussed in lecture for a better understanding) Saturated fats in your diet are associated with high triglyceride and high cholesterol levels which could result in hypertension (high blood pressure) and heart disease. Glycerides are formed when one or more fatty acids are covalently bonded to a glycerol molecule. If there is one fatty acid, a **monoglyceride** results; if two fatty acids, a **diglyceride** results, if three fatty acids, a **triglyceride** results. These are important energy storage molecules in your body and are an integral part of membrane structure. **Steroids** are large (heterocyclic) carbon compounds. The structure will be discussed in lecture class. One of the main steroids in your body is **cholesterol**. Cholesterol is a very important part of your body's biochemistry. It is found in cell membranes. 30% of red blood cell membranes are made of cholesterol. Cholesterol is also a precursor molecule for hormones such as estrogens, androgens and corticosteroids (cortisol & cortisone).

As is true of all organic molecules, proteins can serve as a source of **energy**, though this role is minor. Proteins have many other more important functions. Many **hormones** are proteins, e.g., insulin. Proteins, along with lipids, are an integral part of **cell membranes**. Proteins form the **structural components** of many cells and tissues, e.g., muscle, connective tissue (ligaments, tendons). Proteins **catalysts,** called **enzymes,** are required for the chemical reactions that occur in living things. Each reaction requires a specific **enzyme.** Proteins also serve as **receptors** which initiate many specific reactions in the cells of living things and are responsible for transmembrane transport. Proteins are composed of 20 L-amino acids. Individual amino acids also serve as neurotransmitters (e.g. glycine, aspartate, glutamate), food additives (glutamate), sleep remedies (tryptophan). Nutrasweet (aspartame), is an artificial sweetener made of aspartate and phenylalanine. Proteins are formed when a **dehydration synthesis** occurs between amino acids. The resulting covalent bond, a peptide bond, resulting between **two amino acids** yield a **dipeptide.** If **three amino acids**, a **tripeptide**, etc. When many are joined together a **polypeptide** (a protein) results.

The last group of organic molecules are the nucleic acids. There are two major types of nucleic acids, deoxyribonucleic acid, DNA, which is the genetic information in all cells. (A few viruses have RNA as genetic information, but must convert the information to DNA before making copies of itself). Ribonucleic acid, RNA, is responsible for taking the genetic information from the DNA and converting that information into protein via transcription and translation, processes which will be discussed in depth during lecture.

When experimenting, scientists find many cause and effect relationships. It is imperative for the scientists to develop various tests to identify the chemical nature of the participants in these experiments. The purpose of the following exercises is to become familiar with some very simple tests and techniques employed by the scientist to identify the chemical nature of organic molecules participating in the reactions in living things.

IDENTIFICATION OF CARBOHYDRATES

Benedict's Test for Reducing Sugars: Benedicts reagent is used to test for the presence of reducing sugars. A reducing sugar is one which has a free aldehyde or ketone group located near a hydroxyl group. This hydroxyl group can donate electrons to copper ions (reducing the copper) causing the color of the solution to change from blue to green to yellow to brick orange. This latter color is due to the formation of copper oxide which precipitates on the bottom of the tube. If the aldehyde or ketone group is part of a bond with another molecule, no reaction will occur. All monosaccharides are reducing sugars. Some disaccharides are reducing sugars, some are not. Polysaccharides such as starch test negative for Benedict's reagent.

Lugol's Reagent: In the presence of starch, Lugol's reagent changes from a yellowish-brown to blue black.

EXPERIMENTAL

1. Obtain two test tube racks.
2. Label one test tube rack Benedict's, and the other Lugol's, with tape.
3. Set up 16 test tubes in each rack.
4. Label each tube as to the samples to be tested in Table 2-1. below. Use a pencil and write on the white area on the test tube.
5. Add 2.0 ml of sample to each
6. In the Benedict's rack, add 2 ml of Benedict's reagent to each tube.
7. Mix the contents of each of these tubes with the vortex genie. (Lab instructor will demonstrate its use)
8. Record the color of the original sample plus Benedict's reagent in Table 2-1. below.
9. Place the Benedict's tubes into a boiling water bath for 3 minutes.
10. Remove the tubes with a test tube holder and let cool for five minutes.
11. Record the color of each tube in Table 2-1.
12. In the Lugol's rack record the color of the samples in Table 2-1.
13. Add two drops of Lugol's per tube.
14. Mix with the vortex genie and record the resulting colors in Table 2-1.

TABLE 2-1. RESULTS OF TESTS FOR CARBOHYDRATES

SAMPLE	BENEDICT'S TEST		LUGOL'S TEST	
	COLOR BEFORE BOILING	COLOR AFTER BOILING	COLOR OF SAMPLE	COLOR AFTER LUGOL'S
WATER				
GLUCOSE				
FRUCTOSE				
SUCROSE				
MALTOSE				
LACTOSE				
STARCH				
SKIM MILK				
WHOLE MILK				
7 UP SODA				
DIET 7 UP SODA				
BEER				
EGG WHITE				
EGG YOLK				
POTATO EXTRACT				
SERUM ALBUMIN				

IDENTIFICATION OF LIPIDS

Solubility test - Lipids are insoluble in polar solvents and soluble in nonpolar solvents. For this test, the polar solvent is water; the nonpolar solvent is mineral oil (a mixture of hydrocarbons).

EXPERIMENTAL

1. Obtain two test tube racks. Label one test tube rack POLAR and the other NON POLAR with tape.
2. Set up 16 test tubes in each rack.
3. Label each tube as to the samples to be tested in Table 2-2. below.
4. Add 2.0 ml of WATER to each of the tubes in the POLAR rack.
5. Add 2.0 ml of MINERAL OIL to each of the tubes in the NONPOLAR rack.
6. Add 2.0 ml of sample to be tested to each of the labeled tubes in the POLAR and NONPOLAR rack.
7. Mix the contents of each tube using the vortex genie. Let the tubes stand for two minutes.
8. Examine each tube carefully. Has the sample dissolved in the solvent or do you see two separate layers in the tube?
9. Record your observations in Table 2-2 as Soluble (+) or Insoluble (-).
10. **Save your tubes from the polar rack (water is solvent) for the Sudan Red test.**

TABLE 2-2. RESULTS OF TESTS FOR LIPIDS

SAMPLE	SOLUBILITY TEST		SUDAN RED DYE TEST	GREASE SPOT TEST
	POLAR SOLVENT	NONPOLAR SOLVENT		
WATER				
MINERAL OIL				
OLIVE OIL				
CORN OIL				
CANOLA OIL				
GLUCOSE				
STARCH				
SKIM MILK				
WHOLE MILK				
7 UP SODA				
DIET 7 UP SODA				
BEER				
EGG WHITE				
EGG YOLK				
POTATO EXTRACT				
SERUM ALBUMIN				

Sudan Red test - Sudan red is a lipid soluble dye. When Sudan red is added to a mixture of lipids and water, the dye will move into the lipid layer coloring it red.

EXPERIMENTAL

1. Take the POLAR RACK of test tubes that was saved from the solubility testing and add one drop of Sudan Red to each tube.
2. Mix the contents of each tube using the vortex genie.
3. Wait two minutes.
4. Examine each tube carefully. Where is the red color found?
5. Record your observations in Table 2-2.

Grease Spot test - When grease contacts unglazed paper, the paper becomes translucent.

EXPERIMENTAL

1. Obtain a piece of unglazed paper.
2. Place a drop of sample on the paper.
3. Make circles around the spots with a #2 pencil and write the name of the sample next to them.
4. Allow to dry.
5. Hold the paper up to the light and observe the spots.
6. Record results your observations in Table 2-2.

IDENTIFICATION OF PROTEINS

Biuret Test. Biuret reagent is a light blue solution which turns purple when mixed with a solution containing protein. The purple color is formed when the copper ions in the reagent react with the peptide bonds of the polypeptide chains

EXPERIMENTAL

1. Set up 16 test tubes in test tube rack.
2. Label each tube as to the samples to be tested in the Table below.
3. Add 2.0 ml of sample to each.
4. Add 2.0 ml of Biuret reagent to each tube.
5. Mix the contents of each of these tube with the vortex genie. (Lab instructor will demonstrate its use)
6. Let stand two minutes and record the color in Table 2-3.

IDENTIFICATION OF AMINO ACIDS

Ninhydrin Test for Amino Acids. Because amino acids contain a free amino group, they are readily detected with ninhydrin reagent which reacts with free amino groups to form a purple, violet or yellow color.

EXPERIMENTAL

1. Put a drop of each of the samples listed in Table 2-3 on a piece of filter paper.
2. Draw a circle around the spot with a #2 lead pencil.

3. Write the name of the sample next to the spot.
4. Allow the spots to dry.
5. Ask you instructor or lab assistant to put a drop of ninhydrin reagent on each spot.
6. Wait for at least twenty minutes.
7. Observe each spot carefully.
8. Record your observations on Table 2-3. Indicate the presence (+) or absence (-) of free amino groups in each sample.

TABLE 2-3. RESULTS OF TESTS FOR PROTEINS & AMINO ACIDS

SAMPLE	BIURET REACTION		NINHYDRIN TEST	
	COLOR AFTER TWO MINUTES	PROTEIN PRESENT	FINAL COLOR OF SPOT	AMINO ACID PRESENT?
WATER				
SERUM ALBUMIN				
LYSINE				
ALANINE				
PROLINE				
GLUCOSE				
LACTOSE				
STARCH				
SKIM MILK				
WHOLE MILK				
7 UP SODA				
DIET 7 UP SODA				
BEER				
EGG WHITE				
EGG YOLK				
POTATO EXTRACT				

A special thanks to Drs. Wahlert and Holland of Baruch College for their permission to use material in this experiment from the Bio-1003 laboratory.

3

The Microscope

INTRODUCTION

In order to study the structure and composition of the **components** of the systems, such as the digestive system, circulatory system, reproductive system and so on, that you dissected last time, it is necessary to examine specially prepared sections under the **microscope**. This is because many of the fine details are too small to be seen with the unaided eye.

The basic function of the microscope is similar to that of a pair of glasses used by individuals with weak or faulty vision. It is an obvious fact that the nearer to the eye that an object is brought, the larger it seems to be. The lens in a pair of glasses brings the object to be viewed by the eye apparently much closer to the eye so it can be seen more clearly. The microscope is, in fact, a series of lenses which bring the object apparently so close to the eye that very small objects can be **resolved**, i.e. seen in clear detail. Of course, the object is not really brought nearer to the eye but an **image** of it is focused on the lens of the eye. The property of a lens that is involved here is called **magnification**.

It is of no use to obtain a magnified image which is blurred, i.e. no detail can be seen, so a second important requirement of the microscope, in addition to magnification, is **resolution**. This is a property of the **light source** of the instrument. Resolution may be defined as the ability to distinguish clearly between two points a measured distance apart. For example, with the best microscope using white light, it is impossible to distinguish clearly between two points less than 0.000019 inch or 0.5 μm (micrometer) apart.

There is one further feature to consider when examining biological material, namely **contrast**. The components of living material have to be **stained** with various dyes to **differentiate** one kind of structure from another. You will soon become familiar with examining slides which have quite a wide range of attractive colors enabling you to distinguish different structures within the tissue. Contrast is clearly not a property of the microscope but rather of the procedure of preparing a slide.

LABORATORY EXERCISE

PURPOSE

The proper usage of the compound microscope.

Figure 3 is a diagram of a compound microscope similar to the one you will be using. You should quickly become familiar with all the parts of the instrument and the various names. Your instructor will demonstrate the instrument, indicating the function of each part and then how to use the various objectives, how to focus, how to get the best illumination of the light source. Pay careful attention! Many students miss a lot of vital information because they never learn to use their microscopes well! Do not be afraid to ask questions if you are uncertain what something is for or how to do something.

14

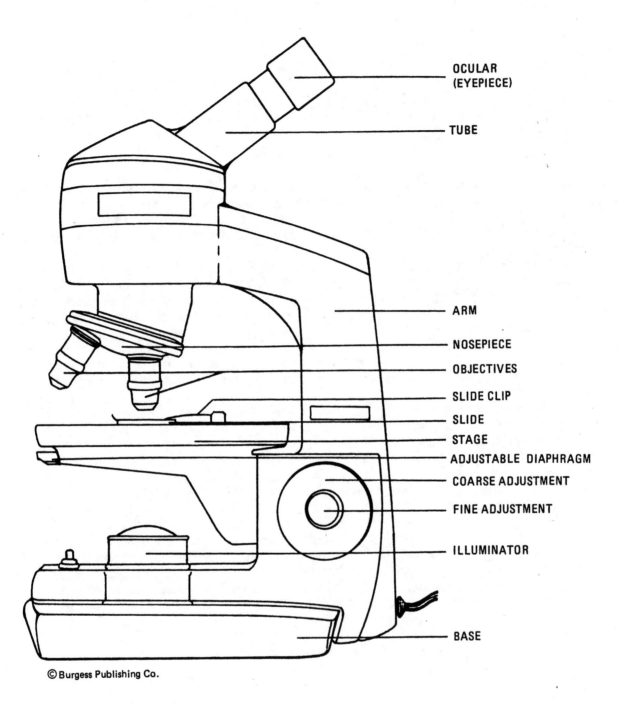

OCULAR
(EYEPIECE)

TUBE

ARM

NOSEPIECE

OBJECTIVES

SLIDE CLIP

SLIDE

STAGE

ADJUSTABLE DIAPHRAGM

COARSE ADJUSTMENT

FINE ADJUSTMENT

ILLUMINATOR

BASE

Figure 3 STUDENT MICROSCOPE, ANGLED TUBE

There follows a description of the functions of the parts of the microscope and directions for some of the more important operations you must perform with the instrument.

A. Functions of the Parts of the Microscope

The **objective** is the heart of the microscope. It provides the **resolving power**, the formation of an image in which the desired details are clearly distinguished. Your microscope is equipped with three objectives of three different **focal lengths**. The shorter the focal length, the less is the **working distance** to the object, the greater is the resolving power, and the smaller is the field or area of the object covered.

Focal Length	Magnification	Field (area)
30 mm or 32 mm	3.5 x or 4 x	large
16 mm	10 x	medium
4 mm	43 x	small

The **initial magnification** of the objective provides an image with sufficient detail but too small in size for comfortable examination. The eyepiece supplies a **secondary magnification** of the image so that the details are separated enough for normal viewing. What is the magnification of your eyepiece? It is engraved on the mount. The eyepiece makes the image larger; does it increase the amount of distinguishable detail? What is the total **magnification** with the 4 mm objective? With the 16 mm? With the 32 mm objective?

Objects are visible because they interfere with the course of light rays. Opaque objects are seen by **reflected light**, and transparent objects by transmitted light. Most slides you will observe will contain transparent objects. The **illumination system**, i.e. light source and condenser, is under the **stage**. The **condenser**, in essence, is an optical funnel; it concentrates the light on the object and fills the field of the objective. The **iris diaphragm** regulates the amount of light allowed to fall on the object for eye comfort and for sharpest vision. The **diaphragm** control is the flat black lever. Do not confuse it with the chromed knurled set screw that locks the condenser into place. The **substage adjustment** regulates the position of the condenser. In almost all of your work, the condenser is best racked all the way up and left there.

For ready interchange, the objectives are mounted on a **revolving nosepiece**. To center each objective firmly in the **optical axis**, the nosepiece has a small spring clip at the rear which engages a notch in the objective mount with a distinctly audible click. Flat objects, such as slides, are retained on the stage by **stage clips**. These are springs loosely inserted in the stage so as to permit horizontal movement of the slide in the focal place. To avoid loss of the clips, make certain that the springs are on the stage and the button parts are pressed down firmly.

The **body tube** establishes the correct distance between the eyepiece and objective and excludes extraneous light.

For rapid changes in objective-to-object distance the stage (or body tube), is moved by a rack-and-pinion arrangement operated by the large **coarse adjustment** knob. More delicate movements are accomplished by the micrometer controlled by the **fine adjustment** knob set within the coarse adjustment knob. The fine adjustment has a limited range of operation which stops at the upper or lower end. Before it is used, it should be set in an intermediate position. The knobs are used for focussing.

B. Care of the Microscope

When you carry the microscope to and from the cabinet, hold it securely, one hand around the arm, the other under the base. This way it is impossible to accidently drop the microscope and find yourself with a hefty bill for repairs!

When you plug the microscope in, note that the plug has to be twisted slightly to engage. It is at the end of the lab, when you are in a hurry to leave, that most damage is done because of attempts to remove the plug without twisting it back to disengage it. Severe jolts to the plug and cord usually end in broken terminals inside the base of the microscope which are both difficult to fix and mean the microscope is out of service when other classes may need it. **Please be careful of this point.**

Everytime you use the microscope you should clean the optical surfaces of the eyepiece, the objectives, and the condenser very carefully with clean **lens paper.** Do not use any other sort of paper, as it may scratch the surface of the lens; use a clean piece for each operation. After cleaning, try to avoid touching and smearing any of these surfaces or you will have to begin again. It is your responsibility to keep the surfaces clean and leave the surfaces clean. Do not unscrew any of the lens systems, eyepiece or objective. If any of these seem dirty inside, ask your instructor to clean it for you.

1. **USE OF THE MICROSCOPE**

A. Focussing the Object

To get used to focussing an object with different objectives we use a prepared slide with a letter **e** cut from newsprint mounted on the slide under a coverslip, a very tiny piece of glass to protect the specimen. Begin your examination with the low power (4x) lens. The objective and stage should be about 1/4 inch apart. Clip the slide to the stage so that the object, the letter **e**, is exactly in the center of the opening. With your eye to the eyepiece, use the coarse adjustment slowly to raise the stage (or lower the objective) until the image comes distinctly into view. Then roll the fine adjustment back and forth until the image is as sharp as possible. Now close and open the **iris diaphragm** until the aperture is found which permits your eye to discern the greatest detail. Note how much of the field is taken up by the letter. Does the image of the **e** appear erect or inverted? Why?

Repeat the entire focussing procedure several times until your finger begins to have the "feel" of the distance the stage (or objective) has to be moved. Now repeat the same procedure using the 16 mm (10x), medium power lens, remembering that your working distance is now less, i.e., the objective will be closer to the slide. How much of the field does the letter now take up? Now move to the high power objective. In learning to focus under high power, it must be remembered that the working distance is less than 1/6th of an inch. With the objective and stage about an inch apart, rotate the 4 mm (43x) objective into place. Watching at stage level, use the coarse adjustment carefully until the objective is as close to the slide as possible without touching it. Now place your eye to the eyepiece and with the fine adjustment focus slowly until the image is clear and distinct.

If you cannot locate the object, and if you find that your objective is more than a quarter inch away from the slide, you probably have passed the focal plane. Therefore, repeat the entire procedure. Place your head at stage level; put the objective in closest proximity to the slide, and start again the fine focussing.

To avoid damage to the microscope slide and to the objective lens when using the high power objective (43x), with your eye at the eyepiece, you should always focus in such a way that the objective lens and slide are moving apart.

When the object is finally located under high power, adjust the iris diaphragm for maximum resolution. How much of the field is now occupied by the letter? Which objective shows the larger field? Which provides the greater resolving power? Which objective would you use when examining an object?

Note: You should soon discover that if you can focus an object clearly, using the 32 mm lens, that it will <u>still</u> be in focus when you swing first the 16 mm and then 4 mm objective round on the revolving nosepiece and click the objective into place. This means the microscope is **parfocal**. Occasionally, due to rough handling by some students, you may find that after focussing, using the 16 mm objective when you swing round the 4 mm objective, the object is now very blurred. Usually you can obtain a sharp picture using the <u>fine focussing knob only</u> and you will find you always have to turn it the same direction. You can soon become familiar with this and it certainly beats having to focus under the 4 mm objective everytime from scratch.

B.   <u>Adjusting the Light Falling on the Object</u>

Try changing from one objective to the other several times. Determine which requires the larger diaphragm-opening, the 4 mm or the 16 mm objective. This will make it evident that when you change objectives, not only must the microscope be refocused, but the diaphragm must also be reset. This is also true when different objects are viewed.

C.   <u>Locating Objects in the Microscope Field</u>

Many of our microscopes have a pointer inserted into the eyepiece which makes locating objects rather easy; all you have to do is move the slide carefully around so that the object you are interested in lies at the pointer. If you do not have a pointer, you can resort to the convention of describing the circular field in terms of a clock face, e.g., examine the part of the image at 12 o'clock; at 3 o'clock; at 6 o'clock, and at 9 o'clock.

You found that the 16 mm field has a larger area for exploration, and that the 4 mm, though providing a smaller field, shows more detail. However, the two fields, while different in area, are concentric. Therefore, an object located under the 16 mm will certainly be in view under the 4 mm if it is first placed in the center of the field. Look at the part of the image now in the center of the 16 mm field. Push the slide toward 12 o'clock. How does the image move? Push the slide toward 6 o'clock. How does the image move? Push the slide toward 3 o'clock. How does the image move? Push the slide toward 9 o'clock. How does the image move? What is the position of the image in relation to the position of the object?

Despite the novelty of the positions, you will quickly find that if your eye is at the eyepiece, your fingers will move the slide properly to bring the desired portions into the field. Apparently, you have long since learned to correct the illusions of vision by the more reliable sense of touch. How do you <u>know</u> (?) that railroad tracks do not really converge even though you see them do so? That the corners of the table are right angles even though you see oblique angles? Revolve the slide carefully about its center in a clockwise direction. In what direction does the image revolve? Do not guess; try this and actually see for yourself. How can you explain this?

D. Measuring Microscopic Objects

The unit used for microscopic measurement is the **micrometer** or μm (the Greek symbols for the term).

$$1 \; \mu\text{m} \;\; = \;\; \frac{1}{1000} \; \text{mm} \quad \text{or} \quad \frac{1}{1,000,000} \; \text{m} \quad \text{or} \quad \frac{1}{25,400} \; \text{inch.}$$

$$\text{(0.001 mm)} \qquad\qquad \text{(0.000001 m)} \qquad\qquad \text{(0.000039 inch)}$$

You will see why it is sensible to use such a term and so avoid all these decimal fractions.

For <u>accurate</u> <u>measurement</u> of the length or width of an object, it is necessary to use a calibrated scale inserted into the eyepiece. However, fair estimates of larger objects may be made by calibrating the width of the field itself. For this purpose take a slide of bolting silk which has approximately 160 threads per inch. Focus the slide under the 16 mm objective. Count the number of squares straight across the field, estimating to the nearest tenth. Then divide by 160 to get the diameter in inches and multiply by 25,400 to convert to micrometers. Repeat the procedure using the 4 mm objective.

When you use the 4 mm objective you have an additional problem in that the thickness of the strands of silk <u>contributes</u> to the field so you must take account of this in your estimation. Always measure from the same point to the same point: (see arrows Figure 4) from the outside of one strand to the outside of the next silk strand is <u>one</u> square.

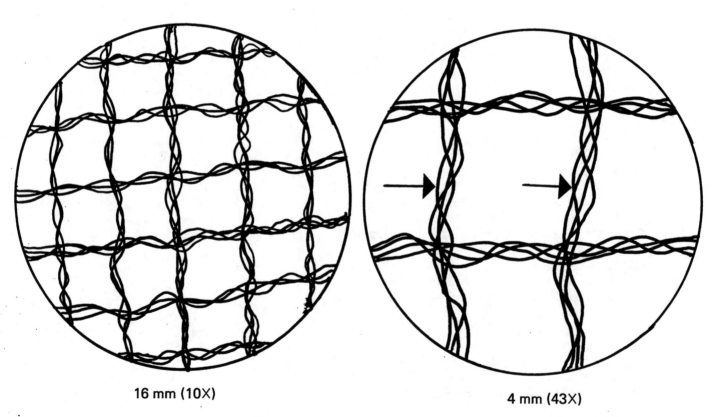

16 mm (10X)   4 mm (43X)

Figure 4 CALIBRATION OF THE MICROSCOPE FIELD USING BOLTING SILK

Record your field diameters in micrometers for use in later measurements:

Diameter of field with 16 mm (10 x) objective is _____ micrometers.

Diameter of field with 4 mm (32 x) objective is _____ micrometers.

To determine the height or depth of an object under the microscope, use the micrometer scale engraved on the fine adjustment. First, focus on the lower surface of the object and take a reading. Then focus through to the upper surface and take another reading. The difference between the two readings is the number of micrometers thick that the object is. How many micrometers does each division on the engraved scale represent?

Your instructor will describe to you how a permanent slide of living tissue is prepared including the stages of: 1) fixing the tissue in a hardening solution, 2) embedding it in paraffin, 3) sectioning it into microscopically thin slices on the microtome, 4) mounting the sections on slides, 5) staining the sections, and 6) covering with coverslips sealed on with permanent transparent adhesive. Why do sections have to be so thin? Why is the tissue embedded for sectioning? What is the advantage in staining the sections?

4

THE CELL - PART I
STRUCTURE

The basic unit or building block of living things is the cell. In an analogous way the basic building block of a house or a wall would be the brick. Most cells are microscopic in size so it is stating the obvious to note that cells were not described until the microscope was invented. Robert Hooke probably invented the compound microscope in the 1660's and it was he who first used the term cell to describe the regular rows of box-like compartments he observed in his studies of cork. They reminded him of the cells that monks used to live in or the cells in which prisoners were held. It was not until 1838 that the **cell theory**, stating that all living things were composed of cells, was proposed by Schleiden and Schwann.

However, all cells are not the same. They become **differentiated** to carry out **specialized functions**. Collections of numerous cells of a similar sort constitute **tissues**. **Organs**, namely, the stomach, kidney, heart, liver, pancreas and so on, are arrangements of specialized tissues. The organs in turn constitute **organ systems**, such as the digestive system, respiratory system, and nervous system. In most instances, cells can be studied only in tissues and organs that are **specialized**. The limitation of these cells is that they are anatomically differentiated for particular functions. In a few cases, isolated cells are available for examination. The protoplasm of which living cells is composed is, basically, **transparent**, so it is often necessary to use various staining techniques to reveal the details of cell structure.

LABORATORY EXERCISES

PURPOSE

During this session, we shall study single cells and cells in tissues, stained cells and unstained cells, animal cells and plant cells. Our purpose is to determine which features are universal to all cells, regardless of their modifications for functioning in special tissues. We will also examine the differences which make each cell studied unique.

A. Examination of Live Animal Cells

Make a **wet mount** of some **cheek epithelial (squamous epithelium)** cells: Obtain a clean slide and coverslip, a dropping bottle of spring water, and an applicator stick. Put a drop of **spring water** on the center of the slide. With the applicator stick, gently scrape the inside of your cheek. This procedure will cause some of the **epithelial** cells to be loosened and adhere to the end of the stick. Now swirl the applicator stick in the spring water to suspend the cells. Use your forceps to lower the coverslip onto the drop of spring water, avoiding bubbles by placing the cover slip onto the drop at an angle.

Examine the preparation under the scanning objective. Note whether any air bubbles are in the field. These will appear as clear perfect circles. If so, observe that changing the focus varies the optical diameter of the bubble and that the light refraction gives the appearance of color. In the future, do not confuse the air bubbles with the specimens themselves. Locate some cheek epithelial cells that are well separated. Note that the cells look like little 'flakes'. Why are the cells so difficult to locate? Since the protoplasm is not stained (as were the frog blood cells observed in the previous lab), it will be necessary to adjust the illumination very carefully. Center a single cell in the field and switch to the low power objective. Note, that because of the increased resolution the 'flake' now looks like a cell. Again, center a cell in the field and switch to the high power objective for detailed study.   Even though the structures are colorless, what makes it possible for you to distinguish the nucleus so easily from the cytoplasm? Is the cytoplasm uniform or granular? Is there any granulation in the nucleus?

Now apply a drop of **dilute iodine solution** outside the right edge of the coverslip. By placing a piece of paper towel on the left edge of the cover slip, the iodine will be drawn under the coverslip and add contrast to the cytoplasm and nucleus. Identify and make a diagram of the **plasma membrane**, the **cytoplasm**, and the **nucleus,** which includes the **nucleoplasm** surrounded by a **nuclear membrane**. Make a diagram of the squamous epithelium cell for review in preparing for practical exams. Label all of the parts very carefully.

SQUAMOUS EPITHELIUM

B. Examination Of Live Plant Cells

1.Onion Epidermis

The surface layer of cells in both animal and plant bodies is called the **epidermis.**

Generally, these cells are firmly adherent, but, fortunately for our study, the inner (upper) epidermis of the storage leaves of the onion bulb is fairly readily removed. In addition, the cells are so stoutly constructed that this epidermis is only one cell-layer thick, making observation of the cell structure fairly easy.

Obtain a small piece of **onion leaf** and observe that the convex surface is smooth and shiny while the concave side has a duller matte appearance. The concave dull side is to be used. With your forceps, carefully lift off the epidermis (this should appear as a thin translucent membrane) and make a wet mount on a clean slide. Employing the scanning objective lens, explore the preparation and note the arrangement of the cells. Are the ends of the cells in line or are they arranged alternately at different levels? Of what value is this arrangement? Switch to the low power objective lens and note the increase in resolution. Select a cell in which the nucleus is clearly visible, center the cell in the field and move the high power objective lens into position. The details will be distinct only if you adjust the illumination carefully. Note the location of the cytoplasm and the nucleus. To increase visibility of the structures, stain the preparation lightly by adding several drops of the dilute iodine solution to an edge of the coverslip and drawing it through with the paper towel as you did with the cheek epithelial cell. Focus up and down with the fine adjustment and observe that the cell is a three dimensional structure with considerable depth. Select a cell which is clearly visible and optimally stained with the iodine. The **nucleus**, located near the side or end **walls**, or in one of the corners, is surrounded by a **nuclear membrane**, which encloses the **nucleoplasm**. Note that in the nucleoplasm smaller circular structures are visible. These structures are called **nucleoli** (singular = **nucleolus**). In this mature cell, the **granular cytoplasm** is only a very thin layer surrounding the nucleus and lining the edges of the cell. Most of the cell is occupied by a very large **central vacuole**. This is seen as the clear area in the center of the cell surrounded by the granular cytoplasm. The **plasma membrane** is firmly pressed against the **cell wall** and usually cannot be distinguished. Make a large diagram of onion cell and adjacent cell boundaries, labeling all parts very clearly.

_____ **ONION CELL** _____

2. *Spirogyra*

A type of plant cell which is conspicuously different from the onion cell is *Spirogyra*, a filamentous alga, found in fresh water ponds, streams and lakes. Place a drop of **spring water** onto the center of a clean slide. With a pair of forceps, remove a few strands of *Spirogyra* from the container and place them into the drop of spring water. Tease out the strands, i.e., spread them apart with a dissecting needle so that individual strands are observed on the slide. Gently lower the cover slip onto the specimen at an angle to prevent bubbles and damage to the specimen. The coverslip should be left floating on the drop of spring water. If there is too much spring water on the slide, blot it dry with the edge of a piece of paper toweling. If there is not enough water on the slide, add spring water to the edge of the coverslip and it will flow under the coverslip. Carefully place the slide on the stage of the microscope with the strands clearly over the lens of the substage condenser. With the scanning objective lens in place, scan the field to observe the general structure. Center a strand in the field and observe it with the low power objective. Note the green spiral shaped structure. This structure is called a **chloroplast** and contains a green pigment called **chlorophyll**. The function of a chloroplast in a green plant is to carry out **photosynthesis**, a process by which carbon dioxide and water are converted to glucose and oxygen in the presence of chlorophyll and sunlight. This process will be considered in greater detail in laboratory exercise 7.

Center a cell in the field and focus the specimen under the high power objective lens. Note that along the chloroplast, there are denser regions. These are called **pyrenoid bodies**, which function in storing **starch**, a **glucose polymer** (a molecule made up of many glucose molecules joined together by covalent bonds). Where does the glucose come from?. In order to better see the pyrenoid bodies, place a few drops of the dilute iodine solution at the edge of the cover slip and draw the solution under the cover slip with a small piece of paper toweling. Note that the pyrenoid bodies will darken, an indication that starch is present. By carefully focusing on the center of the cell, the nucleus of the *Spirogyra* cell can be observed. It is suspended by strands of cytoplasm in the center of the cell. Make a large diagram of the *Spirogyra* cells including all of the structures observed.

SPIROGYRA

3. *Elodea*

The third example of a plant cell to be observed is ***Elodea***, a fresh water plant often grown in home aquaria. Prepare a wet mount of *Elodea* by obtaining a clean glass slide and placing several drops of **spring water** onto the center of the slide. Employing your forceps, remove **one** *Elodea* leaf and place it into the drops of spring water. As before, place the coverslip gently onto the specimen at an angle and place the slide onto the microscope stage. Focus with the scanning objective lens and observe the general structure of the leaf. Center the specimen and focus with the low power objective lens. Focus up and down. How many cell layers thick is this leaf? Are the cells of the layers of the same general size or of different orders of magnitude? Change to the high power objective lens and bring one cell clearly into focus. Note that the chloroplasts observed are round or oval (more typical of green plants than those observed in *Spirogyra)*. Are the chloroplasts in the cytoplasm, the central vacuole, or in the cell wall? You can best determine this by focusing at the middle level of the cell where the central vacuole is seen in its clearest outline.

If you continue your observations for a while, the slide will get warm (why?), and the chloroplasts will seem to be moving. The chloroplasts do not move of their own accord but are being carried along by the streaming cytoplasm. This circulation of cytoplasm in living cells is termed **cyclosis** or **cytoplasmic streaming**. Is the streaming the same direction in all cells? Within a single cell, does the cyclosis continue in the one direction or does it change? Can you see chloroplasts moving through the central vacuole? If you adjust the light you will be able to discern the clear granular strands of cytoplasm carrying them.

In most *Elodea* cells, the nucleus is inconspicuous because it is colorless and transparent while the chloroplasts are bright green and often heaped over the nucleus. If you explore carefully, you will find a cell in which the nucleus may be seen flattened against a cell wall or tucked in a corner. Make a large diagram of the *Elodea* cell and label all parts.

ELODEA

4. General Considerations

Thus far, many different types of cells have been observed in the laboratory. Review your diagrams and your notes and in the following table, note the features observed just in plant cells, those just in animal cells, and those common to all of the cells.

Once you have completed your observations from the laboratory, think about differences and similarities discussed in lecture.

PLANT CELL FEATURES	ANIMAL CELL FEATURES	COMMON FEATURES

5

THE CELL - PART II
DIFFUSION & OSMOSIS

As you have already noted, a chief feature that contributes to a cell's individuality is that it is surrounded by a physical barrier, the **plasma membrane.** The membrane separates each cell from every other cell, even if the other cells are similar, as, for example, in an organ such as the liver. The fact that the plasma membrane is a barrier between an inside milieu (environment) and the outside means that a measure of control can be imposed on what happens within the cell. However, there are some formidable problems posed by the barrier. A major feature that distinguishes living organisms from inanimate objects is the property of **assimilation**, the ability to integrate nonliving materials into the living material or protoplasm. How can the nonliving materials be integrated unless they can enter the cell? How do substances, molecules, get into the cell across the barrier of the cytoplasmic membrane? The barrier function of the membrane is not complete. Otherwise, it would be impermeable, and nothing could get in or out.

In fact, the membrane is **selectively permeable**. Certain molecules pass easily in, or out; others have to be pulled or pushed across the membrane; still others cannot pass at all. The **concentration** of molecules, i.e., the number of molecules in a known volume of solution, is usually very different on either side of the membrane. So long as molecules can move freely, they will move from a region of high concentration toward a region of low concentration until equilibrium is achieved. This is a fundamental principle and the process is called **DIFFUSION**. Diffusion is the net movement of **solute** and/or **solvent** from an area of high concentration to an area of low concentration to equilibrium. At equilibrium, solute and solvent are equally distributed.

OSMOSIS is a special case of diffusion where usually only solvent molecules move, while solute molecules do not (or move much more slowly). In living systems, the solvent is water and the solutes are any molecules dissolved in the protoplasm. **Osmosis** is the net movement of water from a high concentration of water (low concentration of solute), a **hypotonic** solution, to a low concentration of water (high concentration of solute), a **hypertonic** solution, through a semipermeable membrane to equilibrium. Thus the net flow of water is always from a hypotonic solution to a hypertonic solution. If, at equilibrium, the concentrations are the same on both sides of the membrane, the solutions are referred to as **isotonic**. Because the cell membrane is a semipermeable membrane, it is implied that on one side of the membrane there are non-permeable solutes. In order to better understand diffusiom and osmosis you will perform the following experiments.

LABORATORY EXERCISES

PROCEDURES

DIFFUSION

1. Drop a crystal of a soluble dye (solute) into a graduate cylinder filled with distilled water (solvent).
2. What happens to the dye molecules after a period of time?
3. What would you expect the distribution of dye molecules to be after several days? Why?

OSMOSIS

EXPERIMENT- I

Work in groups of four for this experiment.

1. Obtain four sections of dialysis tubing, each 15 cm long, that have been pre-soaked in distilled water. The dialysis tubing is permeable to water molecules but not to sucrose.
2. Make a knot at one end of the dialysis tubing.
3. Attach a string tag to this knotted end of the dialysis tubing, numbering the tubes from 1 through 4.
4. Slip the open end of the dialysis tubing over the stem of the funnel. Using a graduated cylinder to measure volume, fill the bags as follows:

NOTE: WHEN USING ONLY ONE GRADUATED CYLINDER BE SURE TO ADD DISTILLED WATER (dH$_2$0) TO THE BAGS FIRST BEFORE USING IT TO ADD SUCROSE TO THE BAGS! WHY? THEN ADD THE 15% SUCROSE AND THEN THE 30% SUCROSE.

> Bag 1. 10 ml of distilled water.
> Bag 2. 10 ml of 15% sucrose.
> Bag 3. 10 ml of 30% sucrose.
> Bag 4. 10 ml of distilled water.

5. As each bag is filled, force out excess air by squeezing the bottom end of the tube.
6. Now tie a knot at the remaining open end of the bag.
7. Rinse each filled bag in the baking dish containing distilled water (dH$_2$0); gently blot off   the excess water with paper toweling.
8. Weigh each bag to the nearest 0.1g.
9. Record the weights in the following Table in the column marked "0 min".

Beaker #	Bag Contents/ Beaker Contents	BAG WEIGHT IN GRAMS				
		0 min.	10 min	20 min.	30 min.	40 min.
1.	Distilled Water/ Distilled Water					
2.	15% Sucrose/ Distilled Water					
3.	30% Sucrose/ Distilled Water					
4.	Distilled water/ 30% Sucrose					

10. Number four 400 ml. beakers with a china marker.

11. Add 200 ml. dH$_2$0 to beakers 1 through 3.

12. Add 200 ml of 30% sucrose solution to beaker 4.

13. Place numbered bags into their respective beakers as per column one of the above Table.

14. After 10, 20, 30 and 40 min, remove bags from their beakers, blot them dry with paper toweling, weigh them, and record weights in their respective columns.

15. Replace the sacs into their respective beakers and continue weighing until the experiment is complete.

16. Graph your results on the following, plotting weight (gm.) vs. time (min.).

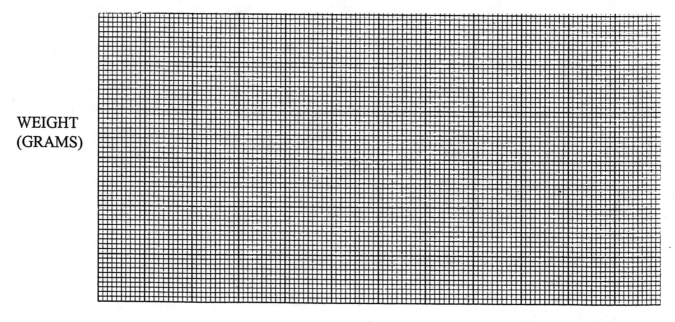

WEIGHT
(GRAMS)

TIME (MIN)

Which bags gained weight, lost weight or remained the same weight? Employing the terms, isotonic, hypotonic, and hypertonic, how can you account for the differences in weight of the different sacs? Remember that sucrose is a non-permeable solute, while water molecules can freely diffuse into and out of the dialysis tubing. Thus, water will go from a hypotonic environment to a hypertonic environment. Which bags are hypotonic, hypertonic and isotonic to its environment?

1. Which bag is hypotonic?_____

   How did you reach this conclusion?_____

   _____

2. Which bag is isotonic?_____

   How did you reach this conclusion?_____

   _____

3. Which bags are hypertonic?_____

   How did you reach this conclusion?_____

   _____

   Why did one of the bags weigh more than the other bag?_____

   _____

EXPERIMENT - II

In the experiment above, you perfomed an experiment demonstrating the net flow of water through a semipermeable membrane employing an artificial membrane (dialysis tubing). What would you expect if you put live cells with a semipermeable membrane (the cell membrane) in solutions of different solute concentrations? The purpose of the following experiment is to test your hypotheses.

Employing *Elodea*, you will prepare three wet mounts, employing a single leaf for each slide. **It is important to blot the leaves dry before suspending them in the desired solution**. Why? On the first slide, suspend the specimen in distilled water, the second in spring water, the third in concentrated sucrose solution. Observe the cells under high power. The presence of chloroplasts in the cell is helpful in demonstrating the function of cellular membranes in regulating permeability. Observe the cells in spring water first.

Where are the chloroplasts? (Do you observe cytoplasmic streaming?) What is the relationship of the cytoplasm to the spring water? Is the cytoplasm isotonic, hypotonic, or hypertonic? Why did you come to your conclusion? Next observe the cells in concentrated sucrose solution. What do they look like? Where are the chloroplasts? Look carefully, and see if you note a membrane around the chloroplasts? Which membrane do you think this is? Why? Did the cell shrink? What is the relationship of the cytoplasm to the concentarted sucrose solution? Is the cytoplasm isotonic, hypotonic or hypertonic? Finally, observe the cells in distilled water.

Employing the fine adjustment on your microscope, focus up and down through the leaf. Note that the chloroplasts can be found along the cell wall. They may be moving very rapidly along the inside of the cell wall. What is this called? When they appear to be in the middle of the cell, it is because they are against the cell wall closest to you or against the cell farthest away from you. Something in the cell is pushing them against the cell wall. Do you ave any idea what that structure might be? What is the relationship of the cytoplasm to the distilled water? Is the cytoplasm isotonic, hypotonic, or hypertonic? Draw and label the cells carefully in the following chart.

DISTILLED WATER	SPRING WATER	SUCROSE

Spring water is the natural environment for the *Elodea*. The concentration of solute in the spring water and the cytoplasm of the cells are the same. Thus, the cytoplasm is isotonic to the spring water, and as you observed in Experiment 1 above, there is no net flow of water between the spring water and the the cytoplasm.

If the *Elodea* cell is placed in a solution of concentrated sucrose, a much higher concentration of solute than the cytoplasm, water will leave the cell, because the cytoplasm is hypotonic and the concentrated sucrose is hypertonic. Remember that water diffuses from a hypotonic environment to a hypertonic environment through a semipermeable membrane. Because of the cell wall in plants, this process, which is called **plasmolysis**, can readily be observed since the cytoplasmic membrane shrinks away from the cell wall. The membrane that you observed around the chloroplasts is the cell membrane. What would happen to a cheek epithelium cell if it was placed into such a concentrated solution?

If a plant cell is placed into a solution of much lower concentration of solute, water will enter the cell because the cytoplasm is now hypertonic. Water will fill the central vacuole. Why? The central vacuole will expand and push the cytoplasm and its contents against the cell wall. This is the reason that the chloroplasts are along the inside of the cell wall. What, then, would be a very important function of the cell wall for a plant in its natural environment? What would happen to a cheek epithelial cell placed in distilled water? Do you worry about this when you drink a glass of water (hypotonic)? Why not?

6

Cell Division-
Mitosis

INTRODUCTION

In Exercise 4 the cell theory proposed by Schleiden and Schwann in 1838, was discussed and you have now seen that the different types of animal and plant material you have observed were all composed of cells. The original cell theory was extended by Robert Virchow in 1859, to propose that all cells arose from pre-existing cells. A moment's thought will remind you that you, as an individual, arose from the zygote produced when a sperm cell from your father fused with an ovum or egg cell from your mother. From that one cell arose the trillions of cells in your body at this moment. The same is true for all animals and plants; they arise from a single cell produced as a result of a reproductive process—the details of that process we will see later in the course.

These million, billions and trillions of cells are produced from that original one cell by the process of cell division. Indeed, when an animal or plant reaches full (adult) size, the process of cell division is not over. It has been calculated that humans lose around 50 billion cells every day from the body by cell death. However, most of these cells are replaced by the process of cell division. You will see from the table below that various cells in the body have very different life spans:

Type of Cell	Average Life Span
Intestine	36 hours
White Blood Cell	2 weeks
Red Blood Cell	4 months
Nerve	
Muscle	Life

The variation in age is often related to the function of the cell, e.g. intestinal cells are in a relatively hostile environment, constantly in contact with digestive enzymes and so do not last long; they are constantly replaced. Muscle cells and nerve cells on the contrary, thrive only by constant use; they may last a lifetime and are never replaced.

Let us look at the process of cell division. As a cell undergoes division, the component parts of the cell, the nucleus and the cytosome, all parts of the cell outside the nucleus, are divided into two portions each. Cell division, therefore, consists of nuclear division followed by cytosome division. Most of what you will observe in the laboratory exercise will concern nuclear division which is an elaborate procedure that accomplishes not only quantitatively equal, but more important, qualitatively equal apportioning of the chromatin of the nucleus. The result is that the two cells formed have the same kind as well as the same amount of chromatin. The process of organizing the chromatin and distributing it to the two daughter cells is called mitosis.

1. STAGES IN THE CELL CYCLE

In killed and stained cells the following recognizably distinct stages can be observed.

a) **Interphase.** This is the metabolic stage between cell division. During this stage, the cell assimilates nutrients and synthesizes enough protoplasm for two cells. In particular the chromatin (DNA and proteins involved in the chromosomes) is duplicated. The nucleus, in interphase, has a **nuclear membrane, nucleoli, nuclear sap,** and **chromatin** visible as granules and strands; however, **chromosomes** are <u>not</u> visible. This stage comprises the major part of the life cycle of the cell.

b) When cell division occurs in the living cell it proceeds in an orderly sequence of activity in the protoplasm. It is convenient to divide the sequence of events of nuclear division into the following recognizable stages.

2. STAGES IN MITOSIS

a) **Prophase.** The chromatin <u>condenses</u> into visible twisted threads, and these further shorten into thicker rods, the **chromosomes.** During this process the nucleolus disappears. At two poles, <u>outside</u> the nuclear membrane, there forms a **spindle** of cytoplasmic fibers. In animal cells the spindle emanates from the **centrosome,** a body consisting of a granule, the **centriole,** surrounded by short fibers. During this stage the nuclear membrane disintegrates. Late in prophase the chromosomes move in a disorderly array toward the center of the cell.

b) **Metaphase.** The chromosomes are now arranged at the **equatorial plate** in the middle of the cell. It now is particularly clear that each chromosome is <u>double</u> and consists of two closely appressed chromatids; in appearance each chromosome seems to split lengthwise. The **chromosomic** fibers of the spindle are attached to the chromosomes at the **centromere,** and extend to the poles. **Continuous spindle fibers** reach unbroken from one pole to the other.

c) **Anaphase.** The pair of chromatids of each chromosome separates starting from the centromere. The chromosomic fibers shorten. The <u>chromatids move apart</u> in two plates to the poles. The chromatids, now that they are separate, are really chromosomes in their own right. Their appearance is very

characteristic at this stage. They look like ∨ or ∪ or ∟ or ∖ shapes,

depending on where the centromere is along the length of the chromosome.

d) **Telophase.** The original chromatids, now chromosomes, once at the pole <u>organize</u> a **nucleus.** A nuclear membrane is established. The chromatin is transformed from condensed rods to a more attenuated condition visible only as granules and threads. The nucleoli are formed and nuclear sap appears.

During telophase, **cytoplasmic division** occurs. In animals, the **cytosome** is divided by **cleavage;** currents flowing in the protoplasm cut the cell in two. In plant cells, the continuous fibers of the spindle partition the cell by forming a **cell wall plate** across the middle of the cell.

Summary of stages: Interphase is the stage of synthesis of protoplasm, in particular of DNA. Prophase and telophase are stages of organization. In prophase the chromosomes are organized and in telophase the nucleus is reorganized. Late prophase and anaphase are stages of migration. During late prophase the chromosomes migrate to the equator. In anaphase, the chromosomes in two sets, migrate from the equator to the poles. The metaphase is a positional stage when the chromosomes are at the equator of the cell.

LABORATORY EXERCISES

PURPOSE—TO OBSERVE THE STAGES OR PHASES OF NUCLEAR DIVISION WHICH OCCUR DURING THE PROCESS OF MITOSIS

Your instructor will show you film loops which illustrate the process of mitosis in living cells.

Although we are mostly dealing with animals and animal cells during this course, the stages of mitosis are more easily observed in plant cells chiefly because plant cells are generally a good deal larger.

A.   Cell Division in the Onion Root Tip

Rapidly growing structures such as the root tips of plants and embryos of animals, are especially suitable for the study of cell division. Obtain a slide of onion root tip. You will note that there are several longitudinal sections on the slide. This is because, when sections are prepared, there is no way of knowing whether a particular tip has numerous cells in active division or not. You should, therefore, explore all the sections and will likely find some showing more stages of mitosis than others. Each root tip has at its end a **root cap** of irregularly-shaped cells. Just above, is the **region of cell division** in which the cells appear almost square in section. This is the region to examine for mitotic figures; do not wander up into the region of cell elongation as these cells become modified for other functions and are not dividing.

Explore the region of cell division of each of the root tips and as you encounter a good example of each stage, correlate it with the diagrams of Figure 9. Label the following: chromatids, chromatin, chromosomes, nucleolus, spindle fibers, cell plate, equatorial plate.

B.   Demonstration of Animal Cell **Division**

Your instructor will set up a slide of the embryo of a developing animal using oil immersion (97X) objective. Do not move the slide in any way. The only thing you may need to do is adjust the fine focus. What stage(s) of mitosis is (are) represented? Observe that the spindle emanates from the **centrosomes**. In the middle of the centrosome is a small granule, the centriole; and the short rays projecting around it constitute the **aster**. Your instructor will move the slide to find other representative mitotic stages. How is cytosome division accomplished in these animal cells? Make a list of the ways in which cell division differs between animal and plant cells.

38

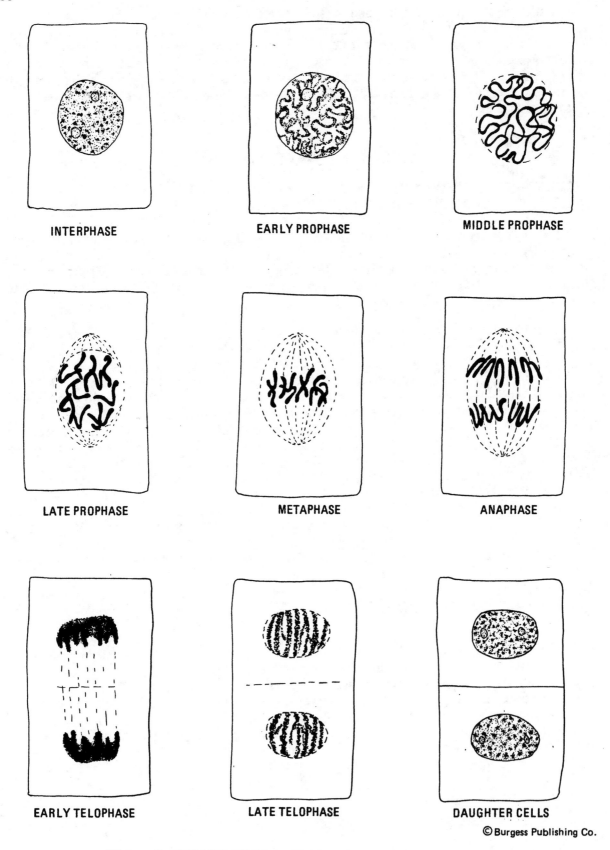

INTERPHASE

EARLY PROPHASE

MIDDLE PROPHASE

LATE PROPHASE

METAPHASE

ANAPHASE

EARLY TELOPHASE

LATE TELOPHASE

DAUGHTER CELLS

© Burgess Publishing Co.

Figure 9 MITOSIS IN PLANT CELLS, ONION ROOT TIP

Animal Cells	Plant Cells

7

Photosynthesis

INTRODUCTION

When we previously discussed those features that distinguish living from nonliving things one of the first things that was mentioned was **movement**. Animals move about basically to get their food. However, plants are also living things. They do not move from one place to another. Why not? The reason is also related to food supply. Plants do not have to move since they are capable of building up more plant material by synthesizing it from simple components in the air and soil around them.

To build or synthesize anything whether in the plant or animal cell requires energy. The source of energy used by plants is **radiant** in the form of sunlight so the whole process is called **photosynthesis**. It is perhaps the most significant of processes found in living things for without it there would be no animals. All animals rely on plants either directly or indirectly for their food and much of this food supplies the energy requirements of the animal. That energy ultimately comes from:

1. THE PROCESS OF PHOTOSYNTHESIS

It turns out that the sources of energy that we use, such as coal, gasoline, and heating oil, are the result of plant and bacterial metabolic activity millions of years ago. The only exception is nuclear energy. These substances that we use as energy were produced by photosynthetic activity so that not just our food but our energy sources are indirectly connected to the ability of plants to convert radiant energy (light energy) into a useful form of energy in the cell, i.e. chemical energy. You might reflect on the wisdom of <u>Homo</u> <u>sapiens</u> in using up in 150 years all the fossil fuels produced in a billion years.

What is involved in the process of photosynthesis? It is a very complex series of chemical reactions leading to the synthesis of carbohydrate (glucose ———→ starch) from carbon dioxide and water, which may be described by the <u>overall</u> equation:

$$6CO_2 \quad + \quad 6H_2O \quad + \quad E \quad \rightleftharpoons \quad C_6H_{12}O_6 \quad + \quad 6O_2$$

carbon   water   energy   glucose   oxygen
dioxide

The oxygen produced is the source of oxygen required in the respiration of animals. Thus you see another reason why photosynthesis is fundamental for animal existence.

The overall equation only tells you what goes in and comes out of the total process and nothing of the various steps involved.

A. Light-Dependent Reactions

Basically, the stages can be divided into those which require light (radiant energy) to work and those that do not. The **light-dependent** reactions occur in the **grana** of the chloroplasts and involve the trapping of light energy by **chlorophyll** and converting it into two chemically useful forms in the cell. This conversion of one form of energy into another is called **transduction.**

The universal chemical compound involved in energy transference in all cells is **adenosine triphosphate** or **ATP.** It consists of the nitrogenous base **adenine** (A) in combination with the 5-carbon sugar **ribose** and three phosphate groups (P).

It is a molecule which can carry energy about and act as the common currency of energy in the cell. We symbolize the molecule: A-P $\sim$ P $\sim$ P. Ths last two phosphate groups are attached by bonds which release a lot of energy when hydrolysed, e.g.

$$A\text{-}P \sim P \sim P \quad + \quad H_2O \rightleftharpoons A\text{-}P \sim P \quad + \quad Pi \quad + \quad E$$

| ATP | water | ADP | Inorganic Phosphate | Energy |

If you look at this equation in the forward direction ———>, you will see how ATP can act as a source of energy. If you look at it in the back direction <———, you will see how ADP can act as a store of energy, becoming ATP in the process.

The other chemical compound, which represents a store of chemical energy and which is produced as a result of the light-dependent reactions, is reduced **nicotinamide adenine dinucleotide phosphate** or $NADPH_2$. This substance is similar to ATP in many ways but is in fact, much more energy-rich than ATP. It is the picking up of hydrogen by NADP which produces the **reduced** form of this compound. The **oxidized** form NADP, is not energy-rich. The following equation describes the overall reaction for production of $NADPH_2$ and also indicates the source of the oxygen in photosynthesis:

$$2NADP \quad + \quad 2H_2O \quad + \quad E \rightleftharpoons 2NADPH_2 \quad + \quad O_2$$

B. Light-Independent Reactions

Utilizing the energy trapped and transduced into ATP and $NADPH_2$ in the grana, a series of reactions not requiring light occur in the **stroma** of the chloroplast and ultimately produce glucose. These reactions are concerned with **fixing** carbon dioxide into the form of organic compounds. A brief summary of events would see carbon dioxide added or fixed into a 5-carbon sugar, thus producing a 6-carbon sugar which splits into two molecules of the 3-carbon compound **phosphoglyceric acid** (3-PGA). By a series of steps 3-PGA can be built up into glucose and starch.

LABORATORY EXERCISES

PURPOSE

a) To examine the structure of the leaf; a major site of photosynthesis in terrestrial plants.

b) To extract photosynthetic pigment from the leaf and study some of its properties.

c) To test for photosynthetic products in a leaf and from a whole plant.

1. LEAF STRUCTURE

Since light is a critical factor in photosynthesis, plants have developed various arrangements of leaves on the stem so that there is a minimum of shading of one another and a maximum of light absorption. We can consider the structure of an individual leaf related to the functions it carries out. There is a large surface area to allow maximum absorption of light and an open spongy network of cells to allow gaseous interchange of water, carbon dioxide and oxygen. This structural arrangement poses a problem, however, as such a large surface area will allow loss of water by evaporation. Indeed it has been calculated that a large oak tree will lose about 400 <u>tons</u> of water a day in the summer time.

A. <u>Cross Section of Lilac Leaf</u> (Syringa)

Obtain the slide and examine it microscopically under first low and then high power. Note that the leaf is bounded by an **upper epidermis** and **lower epidermis** covered by a thin outer **cuticle.** Which epidermis has the larger cells? Do the epidermal cells have chloroplasts? What advantage is this? The cuticle is composed of a waxy-like substance and helps cut down on water loss from the surface of the leaf. Scan the entire epidermis and find the small openings, the **stomates.** On either side of the stomate is a small cell, the **guard cell.** Note that the guard cells have chloroplasts. What is the function of guard cells? How do they operate? Explore the upper epidermis; are there any stomates here? You will encounter an occasional pit gland which is not to be confused with stomates. The stomate leads to a substomatal cavity which is in continuity with the air spaces of the **mesophyll,** the middle region of the leaf. The mesophyll is occupied by **chlorenchyma,** photosynthetic tissue, and interspersed is the vascular tissue of the **veins.** Toward the upper surface, the chlorenchyma consists of columnar cells arranged as a **palisade mesophyll.** How many tiers of cells are there in the palisade tissue? The lower chlorenchyma is in the form of a **spongy mesophyll** with much more extensive air spaces. What is the advantage to the plant in having spongy mesophyll below and palisade mesophyll above? How is this related to the functions indicated above?

Locate the section of a large main vein. It consists of a group of large thick-walled **xylem vessels** above a group of smaller, thinner walled **phloem cells.** Xylem tissue conducts water and minerals up from the root while phloem transports the manufactured organic substances away from the leaf. Surrounding the vascular tissue is a bundle sheath of large soft-walled **parenchyma** cells. Above and below the bundle are supporting thick-walled **sclerenchyma** cells extending all the way to the epidermis. Locate sections of smaller veins. Which tissue is missing?

On the <u>diagram</u> of the cross section of the dicot leaf (Figure 10), label: <u>cuticle,</u> <u>upper epidermis, palisade mesophyll, spongy mesophyll, air spaces, lower epidermis,</u> <u>stomate, guard cells, substomatal cavity, vein xylem, phloem,</u> and <u>bundle sheath.</u>

B. <u>Epidermal Structure</u>

Obtain a slide of leaf epidermis. This preparation was made by stripping the lower epidermis off a leaf and mounting it on a slide and staining it. Note the large clear epidermal cells. They are not sectioned. Therefore, by fine focussing you can make out their three-dimensional structure, and see how they interlock. Distributed throughout are the **stomates** with paired **guard cells** that look rather banana-shaped in surface view. Their chloroplasts cause them to stain more darkly. Around the **guard cells** are

44

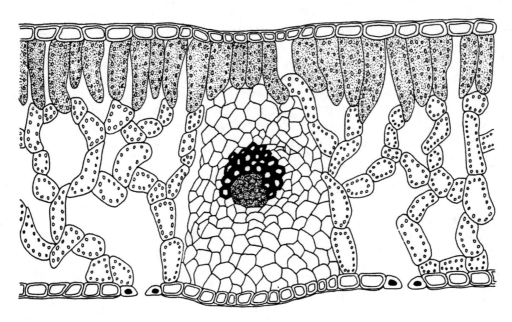

©Burgess Publishing Co.

Figure 10 DICOT LEAF, CROSS SECTION

four modified epidermal cells, the **supporting cells.** Label: **stomate, guard cells, supporting cells,** and **epidermal cells** on Figure 11.

C. Photosynthetic Pigment

As indicated earlier, light or radiant energy is absorbed by **chlorophyll,** the photosynthetic pigment, and the energy is converted to ATP and $NADPH_2$. Chlorophyll appears green because it does not absorb light in the yellow-green region of the visible spectrum. The green is then reflected or transmitted depending on the thickness of the leaf. Its active principle, however, depends on the fact that it absorbs light in the blue and red region of the spectrum. The light energy absorbed by the chlorophyll raises the energy level of the electrons in the active center of the chlorophyll molecule. These high energy electrons are the vehicle for transfer of energy resulting in ATP and $NADPH_2$.

2. **EXTRACTION AND SPECTRAL PROPERTIES OF CHLOROPHYLL**

Using leaves from a Coleus plant, which has obviously other pigments present as well as chlorophyll, we are going to extract chlorophyll from the cells in the leaf.

a) Boil some leaves in a small amount of water in a beaker on the hot plate. Does the water become green? Yellow? What has happened?

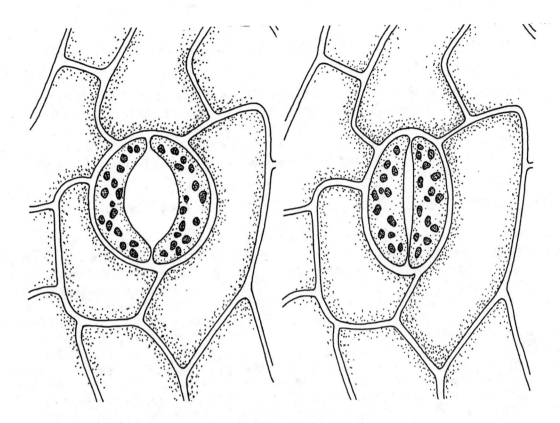

Figure 11 LOWER LEAF SURFACE, STOMATES OPEN AND CLOSED

b) Transfer the boiled leaves to some alcohol and boil gently (a lower heat setting than for water. Why?) Does the alcohol become green? What has happened? What does this tell you about the nature of chlorophyll? What has happened to the red pigment?

c) Use the spectroscope to examine the spectrum of the chlorophyll. Examine the complete spectrum of white light in the spectroscope and note that it is broadly divided into a red band, a yellow-green band and a blue band. Now place a tube containing a fairly concentrated solution of chlorophyll between the spectroscope slit and the lamp. Which light bands are strongly absorbed? Which are transmitted most? What does this tell you about the function of chlorophyll? Could you grow plants indoors under artificial light using a red bulb only? Using a green light source only? Do plants use ultraviolet light? What happens to the radiant energy absorbed by the chlorophyll in the solution? And in the plant?

3. STARCH FORMATION IN THE LEAF

An end product of photosynthesis produced during the light-independent reactions is starch. We will test for its presence.

a) Take the leaves which were boiled in alcohol, wash away the alcohol, and carefully flatten out each leaf.

b) Place a few drops of iodine on the leaf and after a few moments wash away any excess iodine.

c) Observations: What color is the iodine? What color does the leaf become? A positive test for starch is that it will cause a blue or black coloration in combination with iodine. Does the leaf stain positively for starch all over? If not, what does that tell you about the photosynthetic activity in a Coleus leaf? Is the red pigment you observed originally in the Coleus leaf a photosynthetic pigment based on these tests?

4. PHOTOSYNTHESIS LEADING TO PRODUCTION OF OXYGEN

Another end product of photosynthesis, this one produced during the light-dependent reactions, is **oxygen**. Ordinarily, it is dissipated into the air or in the case of aquatic plants into the water. However, we can test for the presence of oxygen with an apparatus arranged to trap the evolved gas. The pondweed Elodea canadensis has been placed under a funnel leading to a water-filled test tube. The funnel placed is in a beaker of water. Any insoluble (!) gas given off will displace the water in the test tube. Two experiments were set up earlier; one was placed in the dark, the other, well-illuminated. Observe the difference in collected gas volumes. A direct test for the presence of oxygen can be done. The routine laboratory test for oxygen is the bursting into flame of a glowing splint. Light a wood splint; blow out the flame; insert the splint into the test tube held upside down. Repeat with the other tube. Is oxygen given off during photosynthesis? How do you account for gas in the unilluminated tube?

8

ENZYMES
PROTEIN MOLECULES THAT ACT AS CATALYSTS

As we have observed, complex animals and plants are composed of cells. These basic units of structure are themselves made up of many different organelles. These are composed of various types of macromolecules, including proteins. In addition to the structural function of proteins, they also catalyze the enormous number of chemical reactions carried out within the cell. Some of these are concerned with growth in general, increasing the components of cells which may lead, for example, to cell division and thus the production of two copies of the original cell. Other reactions may be more specific found only in kidney or liver cells. Some reactions are **anabolic** in that they function in building the components of the cell, or **catabolic** in that they break down components. They may be energy yielding reactions or energy producing reactions. The sum total of all of these reactions is called **metabolism**.

In humans, a modest estimate of the number of different chemical reactions carried out by one or another of the cells of the body is about 10,000. If we were to try to carry out most of these reactions in a test tube we would have great difficulty in getting any but a few of these reactions to work. What is involved in a chemical reaction? Let's take the usual way of representing a reaction:

$$A \;+\; B \;\longrightarrow\; C \;+\; D$$

If substance A and substance B (reactants) are mixed together, they interact to produce two new substances, C and D (products). At the level of molecules, this interaction usually involves forming a covalent bond, i.e., sharing electrons. The reaction described above will not occur unless substances A and B are activated. In a chemical reaction, the amount of energy required for a chemical reaction to occur is referred to as the **energy of activation**. Chemical reactions can be made to occur faster by adding substances called **catalysts**. These catalysts speed up a chemical recation by lowering the activation energy. The catalysts themselves are essentially unchanged by the reaction. Therefore, they are ready again to act as catalysts for unreacted molecules. It is by use of catalysts that chemical reactions occur speedily within the cell despite the relatively low temperature and low concentration of reactants there. In the cell, these biological catalysts are called **enzymes,** which convert **substrates** to **products**. The enzyme lowers the activation energy by forming the **enzyme-substrate complex.**

Substrate (S) + Enzyme (E) $\rightleftharpoons$ Enzyme-Substrate Complex ES $\rightleftharpoons$ Product (P) + Enzyme (E)

Properties of enzymes include:

1. They are proteins.
2. There is a different enzyme for almost every chemical reaction which occurs in the cell. This is referred to as the **specificity** of the enzyme for its substrate.
3. Unlike other catalysts, which yield a major product(s) and one or more by-products, enzyme reactions yield only the specific product(s) with no by-products.
3. Many enzymes require **cofactors** or **coenzymes** to assist their function. $NADH_2$ is an example of a coenzyme. Various vitamins in our diet are required in small amounts and serve as cofactors or as parts of coenyzmes..

1. NUTRITION

If an animal or plant is to grow, it must obtain the constituents (macromolecules) necessary for synthesis of all the components of the various cells of the organism. Plants are able to synthesize all of their cellular components from simple inorganic compounds using radiant energy (sunlight). The process, which was described and studied in Exercise 7, is termed **photosynthesis** and this type of nutrition is called **autotrophic**. Animals cannot synthesize their cellular components from simple inorganic sources. They have to take in, or ingest, complex organic material, food, to satisfy their dietary requirements and supply them with the basic building blocks. From these basic building blocks, which include amino acids, fatty acids and hexose sugars, the animal cell synthesizes all its cellular components, such as proteins, lipids, polysaccharides and nucleic acids, using energy provided by the processes of cellular respiration. The food that the animal ingests is in a much more complex form than the basic building blocks mentioned above. It is derived either directly or indirectly from plants and has to be broken down or digested before its basic components are available for us. This type of nutrition is called **heterotrophic**.

2. DIGESTION

The breakdown of food in the digestive tract is both mechanical and chemical. The chemical breakdown involves many chemical reactions, each mediated by its specific enzyme, and results in the following:

proteins	$\longrightarrow$	amino acids
glycerides (fats)	$\longrightarrow$	fatty acids + glycerol
polysaccharides (starch)	$\longrightarrow$	monosaccharides (hexoses-glucose)

The end products are the basic building blocks of protoplasm as seen above and are in addition, soluble, so that they can be distributed by the blood to the body and, diffusible, so that they can penetrate the intestinal wall and pass into the blood vessels.

The process of digestion begins in the oral cavity and is mainly mechanical (**mastication**). However, chemical breakdown begins there also. You are quite familiar with the experience of increased flow of saliva just before eating some tasty morsel (or even just thinking about it). Saliva is a secretion from the salivary glands which assists the mechanical process of mastication. In addition, it contains an enzyme, salivary amylase (α–amylase), which begins the process of starch (and glycogen) breakdown. Starch is a polysaccharide consisting of many hundreds of glucose units joined end to end to make a very long macromolecule. The action of α–amylase is to speed up the following reaction:

$$\text{Starch} + H_2O \longrightarrow \text{glucose} + \text{maltose}.$$

Maltose is a disaccharide consisting of 2 units of glucose. Maltose produced in the mouth will be broken down into two glucose molecules in the small intestine by an enzyme called maltase.

LABORATORY EXERCISES

The following experiments are designed to show:
1. The principles of scientific experimental design.
2. Enzyme action by studying the effect of the digestive enzyme salivary amylase on starch.
3. The process of absorption of glucose.

You are going to perform an experiment to determine the action of α-amylase. Try to exercise the healthy skepticism and rigorous thinking that characterize scientific inquiry. You will attempt to find out if the α-amylase found in saliva can break down starch into glucose and maltose. Before carrying out any chemical reaction, it is necessary to be able to measure or indicate the presence of the reactants and products, in this case starch and glucose, respectively.

TESTS FOR STARCH AND GLUCOSE

1. The class will be divided into groups. Each group will carry out the following procedures.
2. In separate depressions of a test plate, place 3 drops of each of the following:
   a. starch suspension
   b. α-amylase
   c. glucose solution,(Maltose and glucose are reducing sugars and will undergo similar reactions.)
   d. distilled water. Why is distilled water (dH$_2$O) tested? Remember that samples a., b., and c. are either suspended or dissolved in water. **An experiment can only test one variable at a time**. A test that is performed to eliminate more than one variable is called a **control**.
3. To each depression add one drop of iodine solution and stir with a clean toothpick. Record the color of each mixture on the report sheet below. What is the color of the iodine test reagent alone?

49

Can the iodine solution be used to test for the presence of any of these substances? What is meant by the term color change? Wash and dry the test plate.

4. In separate 10 ml flasks put 10 drops each of the following:
   - a. starch suspension
   - b. α-amylase
   - c. glucose solution
   - d. dH$_2$O.

5. To each flask add 10 drops of Benedict's solution. Place all on a hot plate and watch until they simmer. **BE CAREFUL NOT TO GET TOO CLOSE TO THE HEATING SAMPLES AS THEY MAY SPLATTER AND BURN YOU! USE FORCEPS TO REMOVE THE BEAKERS FROM THE HOT PLATE WHEN THE COLOR CHANGE IS COMPLETED. DO NOT LET THE SAMPLES DRY OUT.** Record any color changes on the report sheet. For which substance is Benedict's solution a test reagent?

SAMPLE TESTED	COLOR WITH IODINE	COLOR WITH BENEDICTS
STARCH SUSPENSION		
α-AMYLASE		
GLUCOSE SOLUTION		
dH$_2$O		

You now have two tests which can be used to distinguish between starch and glucose. You are in a position to mix starch with α-amylase and test for the disappearance of the starch and the hypothesized appearance of a reducing sugar such as glucose or maltose. (As you know from experiment 2, not all sugars are reducing sugars. For example, sucrose, table sugar, is not a reducing sugar.)

EXPERIMENT TO DETERMINE ENZYME ACTIVITY

Most experiments of this type measure some kind of change with time.

Procedure:

1. Each group should put two drops of iodine into each depression of two test plates. Label the depressions on the first test plate from 0 through 11. Label the depressions on the second test plate from 12 to 20.

2. It is important to know that no change would occur in the <u>absence</u> of the test substance, in this case, α-amylase, the enzyme. In order to ascertain this, we must set up a control which does not contain the enzyme. Therefore, each group should put 10 drops of starch and 20 drops of water into a small 10 ml flask and mix thoroughly. Label the flask **C** for **CONTROL**.

3. In addition to flask **C** prepared as described in step 2. above, each group should prepare an **EXPERIMENTAL FLASK,** labeled **X,** according to the following table. Add the starch and water first an mix thoroughly by shaking. To begin the reaction, add the specified number of drops of enzyme solution to your starch and water mixture. Immediately mix your sample and remove one drop of reaction of reaction mixture from flask **X** and place into the depression on the spot plate labeled 0.

GROUP	DROPS OF STARCH	DROPS OF WATER	DROPS OF α-AMYLASE
1	5	15	10
2	10	10	10
3	10	15	5
4	10	19	1
5	15	10	5
6	10	10	10 (BOILED)

4. At thirty second intervals remove one drop from the experimental flask X with the dropper and place into successive depressions in your spot plate containing iodine and note the color. Continue this procedure until there is no color change or until all depressions have been utilized.
5. At this point add ten drops of Benedict's reagent to flask X, simmer on the hot plate and record any color changes. What does this result indicate?
6. Next, add one drop of sample from flask C to iodine in a depression on the spot plate and note the color. What does this mean?
7. Then test flask C for glucose by adding 10 drops of Benedict's reagent and simmering on the hot plate.

RECORD YOUR RESULTS IN THE FOLLOWING TABLES:

TEST FOR GLUCOSE

SAMPLE TESTED	TIME TESTED	COLOR
FLASK X		
FLASK C		

TEST FOR STARCH

SAMPLE TESTED FLASK X	TIME TESTED	COLOR
1		
2		
3		
4		
5		
6		
7		
8		
9		
10		
11		
12		
13		
14		
15		
16		
17		
18		
19		
20		
SAMPLE TESTEDFLASK C		
START		
FINISH		

Discussion Questions:

What effect does water alone have on starch? What effect does α-amylase have on starch? Is starch converted to glucose and maltose in the absence of α-amylase? What effect does α-amylase have on food? Does the experiment prove the existence of a protein; an enzyme; salivary amylase? If you wanted to measure the rate at which the chemical reaction was proceeding, based on what you did in this experiment, what measurements could you make, independently, with time?

DEMONSTRATION OF ABSORPTION

Digestion of carbohydrates is completed in the upper part of the small intestine by the action of pancreatic amylase produced in the pancreas and intestinal maltase produced in the intestinal wall. As indicated earlier, the end products must be soluble and so be able to diffuse across the wall of the intestine into the blood stream. This process in the remainder of the small intestine is called **absorption**. The following experiment, which has been set up for you, is designed to show whether glucose and starch are soluble and diffusible. You will find two beakers containing water labeled <u>G</u> for glucose and <u>S</u> for starch. In one there will be a solution of glucose inside a dialysis sac. This is made of <u>cellulose</u> which acts very much like the cell membrane; it is selectively permeable, letting small molecules across but not large ones. In the other beaker the dialysis sac contains starch. These will have been set up prior to the lab period since as you know, diffusion is a slow process and it is necessary to give the experiment some time to work. Toward the end of the period, test the water surrounding the sacs for glucose and starch with the same procedures used before.

SAMPLE	TEST REAGENT	COLOR
FLASK G	IODINE	
	BENEDICT'S	
FLASK S	IODINE	
	BENEDICT'S	

Discussion Questions:

Did the glucose pass through the dialysis tubing? Did the starch? What would have happened if you had incubated starch and saliva in the dialysis sac?

9

Dissection of the Fetal Pig: The Digestive System

INTRODUCTION

Pigs, as George Orwell noted in "Animal Farm," and as all Miss Piggy fans know, are excellent stand-ins for humans. A 1980 study on the effect of exercise and diet on pigs required sending blood samples to a laboratory. The report back was that these "athletic men were in great condition." This study was, of course, indirectly studying humans by using pigs. Like humans, pigs are mammals, and both, therefore, have anatomical and physiological features in common. The pig serves as a model system for the study of the structure and function of the major organ systems of the body. The digestive systems, in particular, are extremely similar, because both species are omnivores, and thus the diet is not limited, as in carnivores, to animals, or as in herbivores, to plants.

Fetal pigs will be used for the dissection of the **digestive tract**, and in later exercises, for the study of other systems. These specimens were collected from the uteri of pregnant sows killed in stockyards. All are of sufficiently late fetal stages to be nearly or completely developed.

1. DIGESTIVE TRACT

The digestive tract runs from the mouth to the anus. Food is **ingested** or taken in by the **mouth**, where mechanical and some enzymatic breakdown occurs. It passes down the **esophagus** to the **stomach**, where further mechanical and enzymatic breakdown or **digestion** occurs. The waves of muscular contraction which ensure the food moves on, is termed **peristalsis**. From the stomach the partially digested food passes to the **small intestine**. The first region of this, where most active chemical breakdown occurs, is the **duodenum**. This receives two ducts, one from the **pancreas** which produces many enzymes that will further digest the food, and one from the **gall bladder** which collects those secretions from the **liver**, which are mainly concerned with acting like detergents on the fats in the food. The lining of the duodenum produces many enzymes itself. All the digestive processes occur in the **lumen** or space of the tract, so digestion is **extracellular**. The final result of these digestive processes is that **carbohydrates**, e.g. starch, are broken down into **monosaccharides**, e.g. glucose; **proteins** into **amino acids; lipids** into **fatty acids** and **glycerol** and **nucleic acids** into **nucleotides**.

These small molecules, together with vitamins and minerals in the food which were unaffected by the digestive processes, are now **absorbed** along the remainder of the small intestine, through the wall into the circulatory system. The **large intestine** is concerned with **absorption** of water from the undigested food. What is left is the **feces**, which are stored in the **rectum** and pass out through the **anus**.

LABORATORY EXERCISES

PURPOSE

To locate, identify and understand the anatomy and function of the digestive tract.

1. **EXTERNAL ANATOMY**

A. Umbilical Cord

A portion of the cord is still attached to the **ventral** surface. All interchange of substances between the mother and the embryo takes place through the umbilical blood vessels. At the cut end of the cord, note the conspicuous blood vessels, of which the most evident are the one large **umbilical vein** and the two slightly smaller **umbilical arteries.** The cord severs at birth, and shortly after, the part that remained attached to the embryo either dries up and drops off or is bitten off. Mammals retain for life the scar that marks the point of the cord attachment, i.e. the umbilicus or navel.

B. General Body Regions

Note the head, neck, trunk and tail. Make sure you understand which is **dorsal** and which is **ventral.** The head is **anterior.** The tail is **posterior.** The trunk consists of the following:

    1) The **thorax** or chest region, extending from the neck to the posterior end of the last rib.

    2) The **abdominal** region, containing the main part of the digestive, urinary, and the genital systems.

    3) The **ilio-sacral** region, to which the hind limbs articulate. The tail of the pig is relatively short and performs no useful function.

C. Determination of Sex

Before proceeding with the dissection of the pig, determine the sex of your specimen.

    1) Male: There is a small opening just posterior to the umbilical cord. This is the external opening of the urethra. Just below the skin, posterior to this opening lies the penis.

    Ventral to the anus in the male, there are two large bubble-like areas under the skin. These are the developing scrotal sacs into which the testis will later descend.

    2) Female: Immediately ventral to the anus there is a small opening of the urogenital canal. This opening is partially obscured by a triangular fleshy lobe, the urinogenital papilla.

2.   INTERNAL ANATOMY OF THE ABDOMEN

A.   Opening the Abdomen

Place the pig on its back in a dissecting tray. Tie a string to one end of a forelimb, pass it under the tray, and attach it to the other forelimb. Tighten the string sufficiently to spread the forelegs well apart. Be careful not to pull too hard, as the specimens are very delicate and can easily be torn. Do the same with the hind legs.

Make cuts as indicated (see Figure 12). Make the early incisions along the two nipple lines. The cuts should penetrate the body wall but should go no deeper. You can usually tell when the wall of the abdominal cavity is penetrated, by the flow of embalming fluid, which escapes. If the cuts have been made properly, you can then pin back the lateral body wall–flaps.

The body cavity may be more or less filled with coagulated fluid that has leaked into it. If so, wash this out at the sink; be careful not to damage any of the organs.

First examine the organs without disturbing them. Note the umbilical vein, running from the umbilical cord to the liver. After you have identified this vein, cut it in the middle so as to leave recognizable stubs. Then fold the central flap of the body wall (the piece to which the umbilical cord is attached) back between the hind legs.

B.   Identifications

The dissection so far has exposed only the abdominal cavity, which is the posterior division of the **body cavity**. At the anterior end of the abdominal cavity note the **diaphragm**, a transverse sheet of muscle; anterior to this is the **thoracic cavity**, in which lie the heart, lungs, and other organs. Do not, at this time, attempt to open the thoracic cavity.

a)   In the abdominal cavity locate first the **liver**, a very large, dark red organ at the anterior end of the cavity. It is divided into a number of lobes. Gently lift the liver and locate: 1) partially embedded in the dorsal surface of one of the lobes, the **gall bladder**, a storage reservoir for the bile, and 2) the **bile duct**, extending from the gall bladder to carry the bile to the intestine.

b)   Locate the **stomach,** which lies dorsal and posterior to the visible portion of the liver, toward the pig's left side.

c)   Locate the **spleen**, long, thin, ribbon–shaped, and approximately the color of the liver. It lies along the outer curve of the stomach. Compare the shape of this with the spleen of the frog (Exercise 2). Of what system is the spleen functionally a part?

d)   Gently lift the spleen and stomach and locate the **pancreas**, an elongate, somewhat irregular mass of small whitish globules lying somewhat posterior and dorsal to the stomach. This is bound to the stomach and spleen by a **mesentery**, a thin sheet of connective tissue through which many blood vessels run.

Note that all the organs are similarly bound in place by mesenteries. Especially noticeable is the one which binds together the coils of the intestines.

e) Now locate, at the posterior (pyloric) end of the stomach, a ring-shaped muscle, the **pyloric sphincter**. What does this muscle do? The continuation of the digestive system beyond this sphincter is the **small intestine**, of which the first inch or two is called the duodenum. The **pancreatic duct** and **bile duct** empty into the duodenum. The small intestine continues as an irregular coiled tube and eventually leads into the **large intestine.**

f) The major part of the **large intestine** is a tightly coiled spiral—somewhat darker and usually of greater diameter than the small intestine. This spiral can be found posterior to the stomach on the left side of the animal. Push the coiled mass gently to the left and locate, in the dorsal part of the body cavity, the place where the small intestine empties into the large. At this point locate the short blind pouch, the **caecum**. In humans, the thin, worm-like appendix is attached to the tip of the caecum.

g) Bend the coiled intestinal mass gently to the right and locate the posterior part of the large intestine, which appears as a relatively straight tube running along the dorsal part of the cavity and bound to the dorsal body wall. This continues into the **rectum**, which in turn leads to the **anus**, the posterior opening of the digestive tract. Locate this from the exterior. Do not attempt to expose it by internal dissection. Run a blunt probe up the anus into the rectum. The opening and closing of the anus is normally controlled by the activity of the anal sphincter muscles. Label each structure represented by a number in Figure 13.

DO NOT REMOVE ANY ORGANS FROM YOUR ANIMAL!

Those portions of the digestive system which are located in the head and thorax will be studied later.

Exercise 9. INCISIONS 1 THROUGH 7 ONLY. **Exercise 11.** INCISIONS 8, 9 and 10.

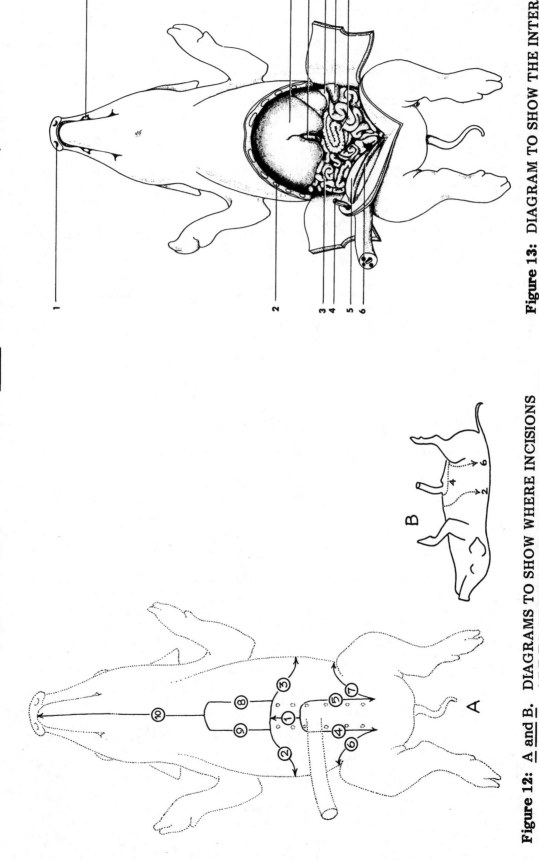

Figure 13: DIAGRAM TO SHOW THE INTERNAL ORGANS OF THE ABDOMEN IN SITU.

Figure 12: A and B. DIAGRAMS TO SHOW WHERE INCISIONS ARE TO BE MADE DURING THE DISSECTION OF THE FETAL PIG.

NAME OF ORGAN	FUNCTION(S)	
mouth		
esophagus		
stomach		
pancreas		
liver		
gall bladder		
small intestine		
large intestine		
rectum		

10

The Circulatory System: Overview and the Heart

INTRODUCTION

The circulatory system is the means by which the **nutrients** from the digestive processes are **distributed** to all the cells of the body. The main function of this system is, therefore, **transport**. In addition to nutrients, the transport of O_2, CO_2, metabolic **wastes**, and hormones depends on the circulatory system.

The circulatory system also plays an important role in protection of the body against infection.

Finally, the constancy of the internal environment is maintained by mechanisms which help in the **homeostatic** regulation of **temperature** and body fluids.

These functions of the circulatory system are made possible by the nature of the liquid tissue, **blood**.

The circulatory system consists of a **closed system** of tubes and a pump which keeps the blood in motion. The pump is the **heart**. **Arteries** are vessels which carry blood <u>away</u> from the heart; **veins** conduct blood <u>toward</u> the heart. The smallest arteries are connected to the smallest veins by **capillaries**. Diffusion of materials to and from the cells takes place through the capillary walls. The constituents of the blood and the fine structure of the blood vessels wil be studied in Exercise 12. The arterial and venous systems will be described in Exercise 11. In this chapter, the structure and function of the heart will be the main object of study.

LABORATORY EXERCISE

PURPOSE

To learn the anatomy of the heart; to correlate the structure of the heart to the pattern of blood flow to and from the body and the lungs.

1. **THE STRUCTURE OF THE HEART**

A. <u>The Four Chambers Of The Heart</u>

   1) Two **ventricles**, which form the greater part of the mass of the heart. The line of division between the right and left ventricles, although not prominent externally, can be distinguished. The muscular action of the ventricles powers the pumping of the blood away from the heart.

   2) Two **atria** (singular: **atrium**) are smaller, thin walled chambers anterior to the ventricles. In the mammalian heart, the wall of each atrium bulges out in a flap, the **auricle**, which serves to increase the volume of the atrium. The atria are the receiving chambers for the blood returning to the heart.

B.   Observation Of The Heart

The heart of the fetal pig is too small for ready observation of its parts. Obtain two sheep hearts, one whole, the other hemisected.

The apex of the heart is formed by the left ventricle. Using this as a landmark, locate the right ventricle and the two atria.

Entering the right atrium are the anterior (superior) and posterior (inferior) **vena cavae.** Entering the left atrium are the right and left **pulmonary veins.**

Locate the pulmonary **aorta** leaving the right ventricle and branching into the left and right pulmonary arteries. Note the arch of the **systemic aorta** leaving the left ventricle.

Correlate the structures you see with the drawing of the heart (Figure 14). Not all of the blood vessels will be intact and visible.

Examine the hemisected heart (Figure 15). Which ventricle has the thicker wall? Locate the openings of the blood vessels within the chambers of the heart. Examine the **bicuspid** valve (between left atrium and left ventricle) and the **tricuspid** valve (between right atrium and right ventricle). These are flap valves anchored by tendons. What are the functions of these valves? Note the tendon cords which prevent the valves from being forced "inside-out."

Locate the **semi-lunar valves** in the aortae. These valves prevent blood from flowing back into the ventricles.

2.   SYSTEMIC AND PULMONARY CIRCULATION

A.   Circulation In The Adult

Examine the models and charts until you thoroughly understand the pattern of flow of blood from the heart to the lungs and back to the heart as well as from the heart to the body and back. Remember that oxygenated blood from the lungs enters the left atrium and is pumped to the body by the left ventricle. Fill in the following chart:

ADULT HEART CHAMBERS	BLOOD VESSEL(S)	OXYGEN LEVEL
to right atrium		
from right ventricle		
to left atrium		
from left ventricle		

B.   Circulation In The Fetus

Study Figure 16 carefully, and note the difference in the pattern of the flow of blood between fetal and adult circulation.

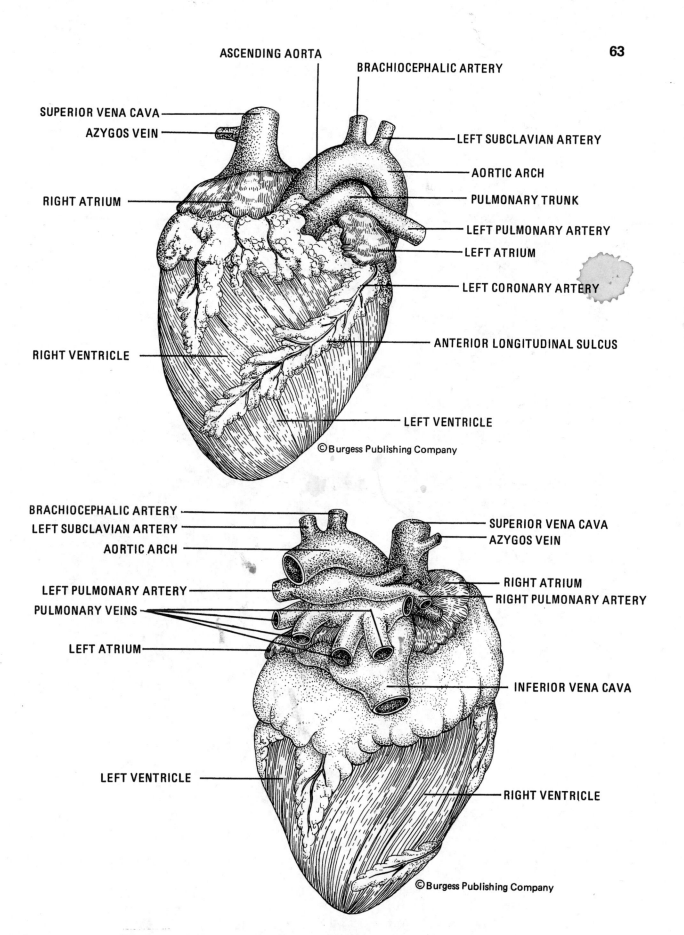

Figure 14 SHEEP HEART, VENTRAL AND DORSAL VIEWS

64

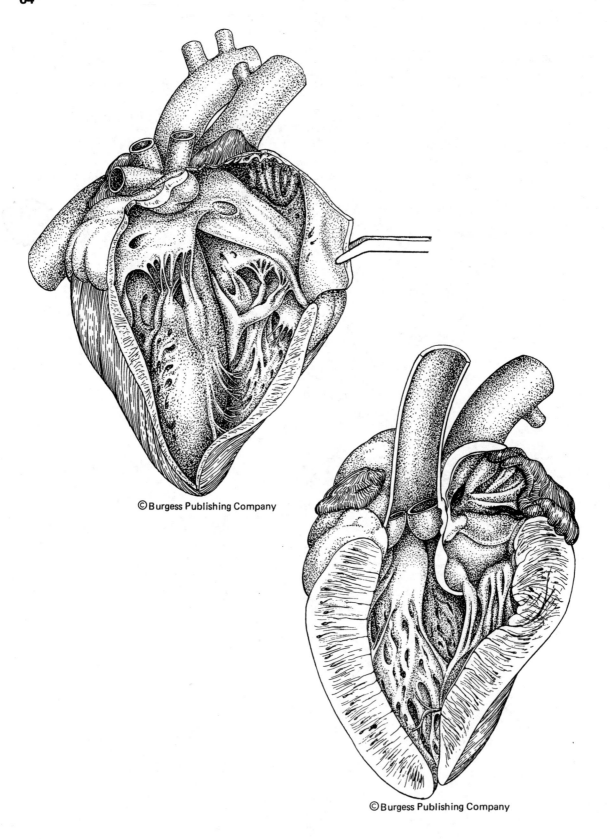

©Burgess Publishing Company

©Burgess Publishing Company

Figure 15 SHEEP HEART, INTERNAL STRUCTURE

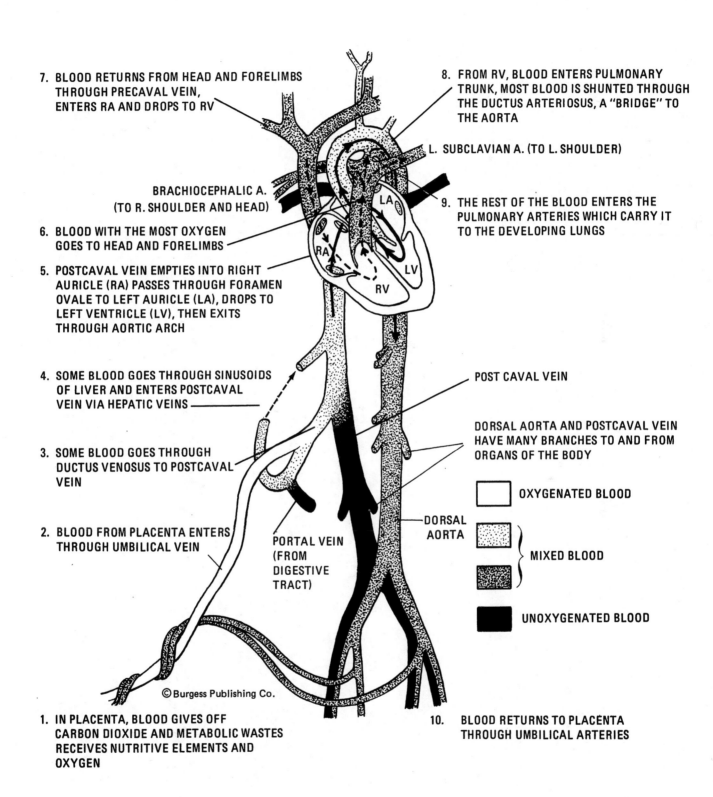

7. BLOOD RETURNS FROM HEAD AND FORELIMBS THROUGH PRECAVAL VEIN, ENTERS RA AND DROPS TO RV

BRACHIOCEPHALIC A. (TO R. SHOULDER AND HEAD)

6. BLOOD WITH THE MOST OXYGEN GOES TO HEAD AND FORELIMBS

5. POSTCAVAL VEIN EMPTIES INTO RIGHT AURICLE (RA) PASSES THROUGH FORAMEN OVALE TO LEFT AURICLE (LA), DROPS TO LEFT VENTRICLE (LV), THEN EXITS THROUGH AORTIC ARCH

4. SOME BLOOD GOES THROUGH SINUSOIDS OF LIVER AND ENTERS POSTCAVAL VEIN VIA HEPATIC VEINS

3. SOME BLOOD GOES THROUGH DUCTUS VENOSUS TO POSTCAVAL VEIN

2. BLOOD FROM PLACENTA ENTERS THROUGH UMBILICAL VEIN

PORTAL VEIN (FROM DIGESTIVE TRACT)

1. IN PLACENTA, BLOOD GIVES OFF CARBON DIOXIDE AND METABOLIC WASTES RECEIVES NUTRITIVE ELEMENTS AND OXYGEN

8. FROM RV, BLOOD ENTERS PULMONARY TRUNK, MOST BLOOD IS SHUNTED THROUGH THE DUCTUS ARTERIOSUS, A "BRIDGE" TO THE AORTA

L. SUBCLAVIAN A. (TO L. SHOULDER)

9. THE REST OF THE BLOOD ENTERS THE PULMONARY ARTERIES WHICH CARRY IT TO THE DEVELOPING LUNGS

LA

RA

LV

RV

POST CAVAL VEIN

DORSAL AORTA AND POSTCAVAL VEIN HAVE MANY BRANCHES TO AND FROM ORGANS OF THE BODY

OXYGENATED BLOOD

DORSAL AORTA

MIXED BLOOD

UNOXYGENATED BLOOD

10. BLOOD RETURNS TO PLACENTA THROUGH UMBILICAL ARTERIES

© Burgess Publishing Co.

Figure 16 CIRCULATION IN THE FETUS

11

The Circulatory System:
Dissection of the Fetal Pig

INTRODUCTION

The circulatory system has two main subdivisions. The first is the closed system in which the blood flows. The larger vessels are the **arteries** and **veins**. These branch into smaller and smaller vessels, the smallest being the **capillaries**. Exchange of nutrients, gases, wastes and other material carried by the blood occurs through the capillary walls into and out of the cells. In dissecting the circulatory system of the fetal pig, we will trace the major vessels only.

The second subdivision, the **lymphatic** system, is important for immune protection, transport of certain fat soluble substances and general water balance. Although it will not be studied, you should be aware of its importance and place in the circulatory system.

LABORATORY EXERCISES

PURPOSE

You will examine the major arteries and veins in the fetal pig. Keep in mind that there will be several differences between the circulatory system of this animal and that of an adult. Also keep in mind that this is a **closed system**, although only the larger vessels will be <u>exposed</u> and <u>traced</u> to the organs they supply with blood.

1. INTERNAL ANATOMY OF THE THORAX

Refer to Figure 12, Exercise 9.

Open the thoracic cavity by making two parallel cuts, one on each side of the sternum. These cuts should extend from the abdominal cavity through the ribs to the base of the neck. Free the edges of the **diaphragm** where it is attached to the ribs. Fold the flaps out to the sides, breaking or cutting the ribs if necessary. Pin them down. The remaining mid-ventral section of the body wall should be freed from its underlying connections and lifted off, posterior end first. Use the scalpel very lightly in freeing it, being careful not to damage any deeper-lying structure.

The large **thoracic cavity** is subdivided into a number of smaller cavities. These are:

1) Two (a right and a left) **pleural cavivities**, each containing (all or most of) a lung;

2) A **mediastinal cavity** between the two pleural cavities. It contains the **thymus** as well as parts of the esophagus, of the systemic (dorsal) aorta, and of the posterior vena cava. Within it also is a fourth division of the thoracic cavity, namely:

3) The **pericardial cavity.** This cavity is separated from the larger mediastinal cavity by the pericardial membrane which encloses the heart. Frequently, the septa separating the pleural cavities from the mediastinal are destroyed in opening the thorax.

Before removing the pericardial membrane (in order to observe the heart and blood vessels), identify the **thymus;** a large soft mass lying ventral and somewhat anterior to the heart. The thymus functions during early life as part of the immune system.

2. DISSECTION OF THE HEART AND CONNECTING BLOOD VESSELS

Remove the pericardial membrane, being very careful not to break any of the veins or arteries connected with the heart. The veins are easily overlooked and broken, since they are thin-walled and look somewhat like folded mesenteric tissue.

Completely expose the heart and identify the two **atria** with their attached auricles, and the two **ventricles.** Then identify and locate the following blood vessels:

1) The **anterior vena cava,** which leads into the right atrium. It is attached to the right side of the dorsal surface of the atrium, a little anterior to its middle. Like all the veins, it is a thin-walled vessel and, although large, it is not nearly so easily seen as the large arteries. It carries blood from the head and shoulder regions. Locate it.

2) The **posterior vena cava,** which enters the right atrium just posterior to the entrance of the anterior vena cava. It carries blood from the liver, trunk, and hind legs.

3) The **pulmonary aorta** (pulmonary trunk), which arises from the anterior end of the right ventricle. It passes forward and obliquely to the left, branching into the two pulmonary **arteries** which carry blood to the lungs. Find the one going to the left lung only. As it is partially hidden from your ventral ispection, carefully, push aside the heart and other blood vessels to see it. The blood returns to the heart through the pulmonary veins, which empty into the left atrium.

4) The **ductus arteriosus.** In your specimen, locate a short vessel that connects the pulmonary and systemic aorta (see #5 below) where they lie close together. This is the **ductus arteriosus,** a straight, short continuation of the pulmonary aorta beyond the point where it branches to form the right and left pulmonary arteries. The duct runs into the systemic aorta and carries blood from the pulmonary into the systemic aorta. It begins to grow smaller in late fetal life and closes sometime after birth. What would be the disadvantage of it remaining open?

5) The **systemic aorta.** The systemic aorta is the major artery distributing blood to the body. It arises from the anterior end of the left ventricle just dorsal to the pulmonary aorta. It extends but a short distance forward before it bends to the left and dorsally to run down the dorsal wall of the thoracic and abdominal cavities. The dorsal, curving, anterior portion is frequently called the **aortic arch.** Due to its location, the portion running along the thoracic and abdominal wall is called the dorsal aorta.

3. BRANCHES OF THE SYSTEMIC AORTA

After the systemic aorta leaves the left ventricle, it distributes blood to the various body regions by branches. Trace the aorta throughout its length and locate the following branches. As you find them, label them on Figure 17.

1) **Brachiocephalic (innominate) artery**, the first branch to arise from the anterior part of the aortic arch. Its course is short, since it soon divides into several branches. These are: (a) the right **subclavian artery;** (b) the **right common carotid artery** and (c) the **left common carotid artery.** Trace these for some distance in order to be able to demonstrate the regions to which they carry blood.

2) The **left subclavian artery**, which arises from the aortic arch just beyond the origin of the brachiocephalic. Trace it to the foreleg.

3) The **coronary arteries.** The heart needs a constant supply of oxygen to function efficiently so a branch from the systemic aorta serves the heart itself. Note the small arteries running around and along the ventricles of the heart. These are the coronary arteries.

4) Just after passing through the diaphragm the dorsal aorta gives rise to the **coeliac artery,** which supplies blood to the stomach, spleen, and liver.

5) Just posterior to this, about 1 cm back of the coeliac artery, the **anterior mesenteric artery** arises and supplies the pancreas, the small intestine, and the large intestine. As its name implies, this artery runs in the great mesentery that holds these organs in place.

6) The paired **renal arteries** supply the kidneys and adrenal glands.

7) The small paired gonadic arteries supply the gonads. In the male they are known as **spermatics** and run to the testes within the scrotal sacs; in the female, they are called **utero-ovarian arteries** and have two branches, the **ovarian artery** to the ovary, and the **uterine artery** to the uterus and oviduct.

8) The **posterior mesenteric artery** arises just posterior to the gonadic arteries. It supplies the lower end of the colon and the rectum.

9) In the posterior part of the abdominal cavity the dorsal aorta gives rise to two pairs of **iliac arteries.** The anterior pair,

10) The **external iliacs,** carry blood to the legs. The posterior pair,

11) The **internal iliacs,** each divides, the larger branch, running alongside the bladder, becomes the **umbilical artery** leading to the placenta; the smaller branch supplies blood to the urinary bladder, and the rectum.

12) The **caudal artery** is a continuation of the dorsal aorta beyond the iliacs. It supplies blood to the region of the anus and to the tail.

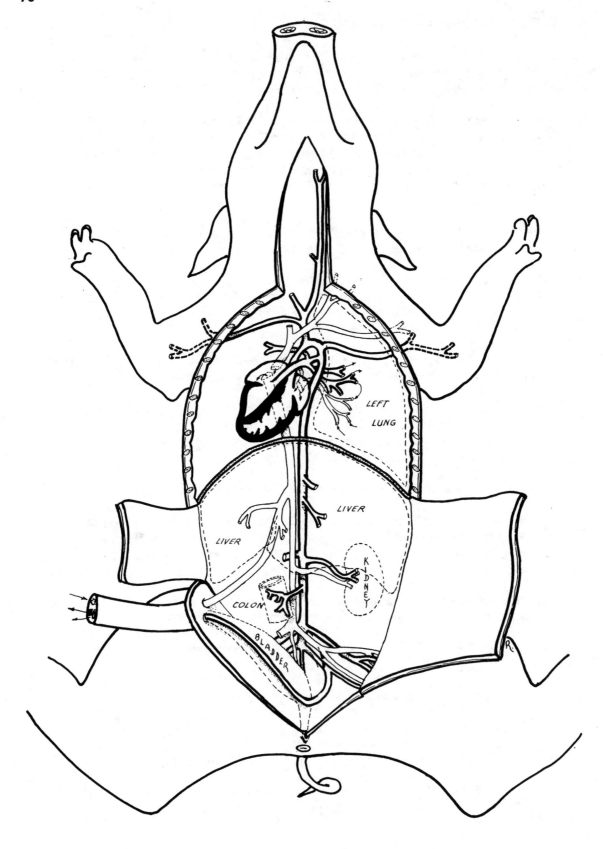

Figure 17 CIRCULATORY SYSTEM OF THE FETAL PIG

4. **VEINS**

1) The **umbilical vein.** Extending through the umbilical cord and through the ventral body wall into the abdominal cavity is the large **umbilical vein.** This vein was cut early in the dissection of the specimen. It passes anteriorly to enter the liver, where it connects with the venous system. In it oxygenated blood and food from the placenta are brought to the fetus.

2) Other veins. Blood from the posterior regions reaches the heart via one of two routes.

   a) Blood from the hind legs, posterior body wall, kidneys, etc., is drained by various smaller veins into the post cava, which runs forward through the liver without breaking into capillaries. Locate the **posterior vena cava** ventral to the dorsal aorta in the region of the kidneys. (This is most easily done by pushing the digestive tract, etc., to the left in the region of the kidneys). Trace it as far as the liver. You have already seen where it empties into the right atrium.

   b) Blood from the organs of the digestive system is drained by several veins into a common trunk, the **hepatic portal vein.** This runs to the liver through the mesentery connecting the duodenum and liver. It roughly parallels the bile duct. In the liver, the hepatic portal vein breaks up into many very small branches and capillaries, which distribute blood to the tissues of the liver. From these the blood is drained into the **hepatic vein,** which empties into the **posterior vena cava** as the latter passes through the liver. In the fetus, the umbilical vein also empties into the **posterior vena cava** close to the hepatic vein. Some of the blood from the hepatic portal flows directly via the **ductus venosus** into the umbilical vein and thus does not go into the hepatic capillaries. In the anterior end of the **posterior vena cava** all of the blood from the posterior regions, mixed with blood from the placenta, flows into the right atrium and there mixes with the blood from the **anterior vena cava.** Label as many veins as you have seen, on Figure 18.

72

Blood Distribution in Mammals

ORGAN	VESSELS TO ORGAN	VESSELS FROM ORGAN
heart muscle		
adult lungs		
small intestine		
large intestine		
liver		
spleen		
kidneys		
brain		
arms		
legs		
uterus		
placenta		

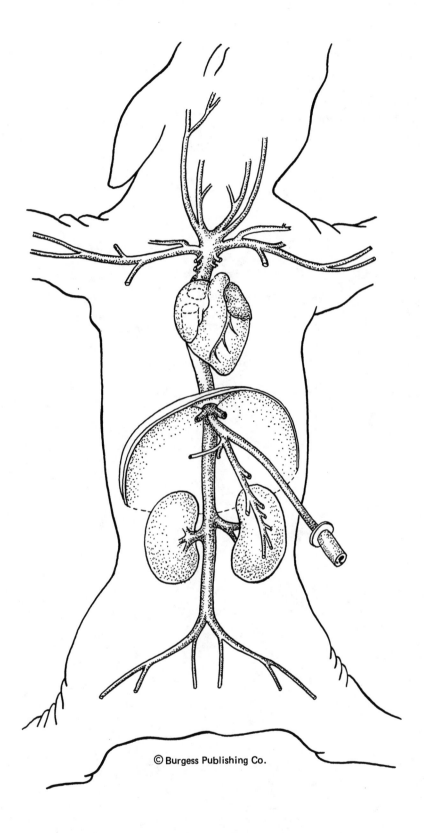

Figure 18 FETAL PIG, MAJOR VEINS

12

The Circulatory System: The Blood and Conclusion

INTRODUCTION

In Exercises 10 and 11, the anatomy of the circulatory system was investigated. The structure of the heart and the pathway of the blood through the arteries and veins was studied through dissection. The functioning of the circulatory system will be the focus of study in this exercise.

The main function of the circulatory system is transport. This is accomplished through the special nature of the **blood**. The liquid portion of the blood is called **plasma**. Plasma is water in which are dissolved the blood proteins, salts, nutrients, nitrogenous wastes, hormones and clotting factors. The plasma proteins can be subdivided into three major classes: **albumin, fibrinogen**, and the **globulins**. Albumin is important in maintaining **osmotic pressure** between the blood and the tissue fluid. Fibrinogen plays a role in the **clotting** process. The globulins, particularly the **immunoglobulins**, are key components of the **immunological** defenses. Other globulins extend the transport properties of the blood; one example is the **lipoproteins**, which regulate plasma cholesterol levels.

The plasma portion of the blood is in equilibrium with tissue fluids and with the **lymph**. It is through the lymphatic system that this protein-containing fluid, which leaks through capillary walls to become tissue fluid, eventually returns to the blood vessels. The lymphatic system is, in addition, part of the **immune system**. The defense of the body is a second important function of the circulatory system.

The cellular portion of the blood consists of **erythrocytes** (red blood cells) and **leucocytes** (white blood cells). In addition, there are cellular fragments, **thrombocytes** (platelets), needed for the clotting reaction. The erythrocytes are concerned with **transport** of O_2 and CO_2; the leucocytes with **defense**.

Heartbeat and heart rate studies are a measure of the functioning of the entire **cardiovascular** system: the pumping of the blood by the heart through the blood vessels. We will conclude this exercise by doing such measurements. These measurements in turn can be related to the general level of **fitness** and to the response of the cardiovascular system to **stress**.

LABORATORY EXERCISE

PURPOSE

In this period, the study of the circulatory system will be concluded with observations of the structure of the blood vessels and the cells of the blood, and these will be correlated with the function of the system. Some measurements of your own system will be performed as an indication of cardiovascular function.

A. Structure Of The Blood Vessels

Examine the slide showing a cross section of an **artery** and a **vein**. The artery has a thick muscular wall, and a large layer of elastic connective tissue. These same layers are thinner in the vein. What accounts for the difference?

B. The Capillaries

Examine the demonstration of the flow of blood through the **capillaries** of the tongue of an anesthetized frog. How does the diameter of the capillary compare with the size of the red blood cells? Is the blood flow steady or intermittent?

C. Constituents of Blood

Blood is a liquid tissue consisting of a liquid (plasma) in which cells are suspended. Nutrients, nitrogenous wastes, plasma proteins and salts are carried in the plasma. The red blood cells, the **erythrocytes**, which account for approximately half the volume of blood, carry most of the oxygen and carbon dioxide.

Examine the slide of stained human blood. The white blood cells, **leucocytes**, are large and have a nucleus. There are several kinds of leucocytes (Figure 19). The large granular leucocytes are able to **phagocytosize**, and thus defend against foreign particles, such as bacteria. The **monocytes** and **lymphocytes** are also concerned with wound healing and immunological functions. The red blood cells are much more numerous. The red color is due to **hemoglobin**, an iron-containing protein which binds oxygen. They appear to have light centers. Do they have nuclei? How long can such cells live? Where are blood cells produced?

D. Heart Sounds

Obtain a stethoscope and listen to your own heart beat. During each beat of the heart, two sounds can be heard. The first is low pitched; the second is sharper, louder, higher pitched and of shorter duration. The first sound is the closing of the atrioventricular valves as the ventricles contract (**systole**). As the ventricles contract the blood is forced into both the elastic systemic aorta and the pulmonary aorta under high pressure. When the ventricles relax (**diastole**) the contraction of the aortae forces the semi-lunar valves to close. This produces the second sound. By listening to these sounds, a physician can detect any defective valve action.

E. Blood Pressure

Your instructor will demonstrate one of the methods of measuring arterial blood pressure. The walls of the arteries are subjected to the pressure produced by the contractions of the heart. A blood pressure of 120 means that as the heart contracts, it pushes the blood against the walls of the radial artery of the arm with a force sufficient to raise a column of mercury 120 millimeters. This is equal to a force of about 2.3 pounds over each square inch of arterial surface. Where would you expect blood pressure to be highest? Lowest? How does this correspond with the thickness of the walls of veins and arteries? How would blood pressure vary as the ventricles contract and relax?

F. Effect Of Work On Heart Rate

The rate of the contraction of the ventricles can also be determined by measuring the rate of the contraction wave along an artery (the **pulse**).

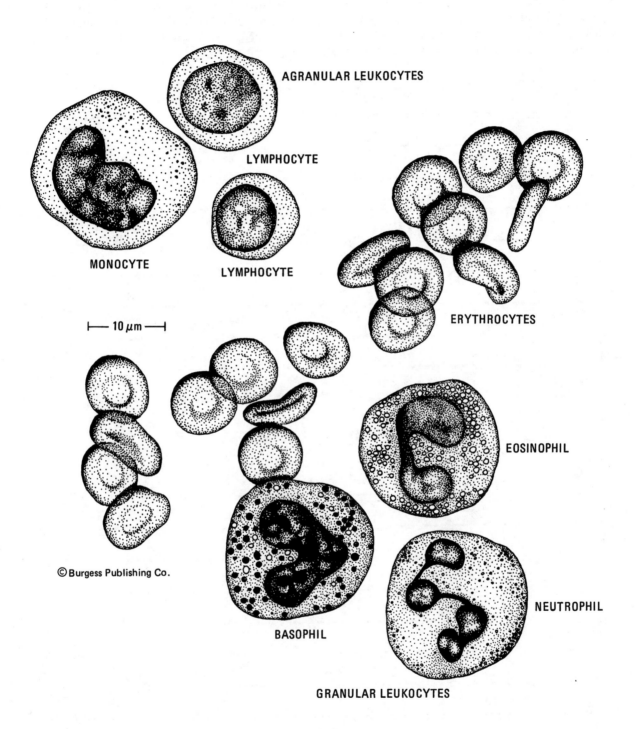

AGRANULAR LEUKOCYTES

LYMPHOCYTE

MONOCYTE

LYMPHOCYTE

├── 10 μm ──┤

ERYTHROCYTES

EOSINOPHIL

© Burgess Publishing Co.

NEUTROPHIL

BASOPHIL

GRANULAR LEUKOCYTES

Figure 19 HUMAN BLOOD CELL TYPES

Place your fingertips over the inner side of the wrist below the base of the thumb. Count the pulsations of the radial artery for the one minute. Record the count on the chart. Repeat the observation four times and take an average of the five counts.

Do fifteen deep knee bends as rapidly as you can. Without delay begin a series of ten measurements of your pulse rate. Allow a lapse of one minute between successive readings. Record your data and make a graph of the results.

MEASUREMENT OF HEART RATE	
Pulse Rate at Rest	Reading
count 1	
" 2	
" 3	
" 4	
" 5	
average of 5 counts:	
Pulse Rate After Exercise	
1	
2	
3	
4	
5	
6	
7	
8	
9	
10	

13

The Respiratory Tract

INTRODUCTION

The respiratory system is the organ system through which gas exchange, namely of **oxygen** and **carbon dioxide** occurs. Respiration can be considered on three levels.

External respiration is the movement of oxygen and carbon dioxide to and from the surface of the respiratory membranes. This is the main function of the **respiratory tract**.

Internal respiration is the exchange of gases across cell membranes. This is an important function of the blood.

Cellular respiration involves the production of chemical energy, ATP, and $NADH_2$. Oxygen is consumed and carbon dioxide is evolved during the processes involved.

The exchange of gases across respiratory and cellular surfaces occurs by diffusion. The gases move across the membranes in solution, hence these surfaces must be moist. This poses no problem for aquatic organisms. However, in humans and other terrestrial organisms the respiratory tract is designed to <u>humidify</u>, <u>clean</u> and <u>warm</u> the air, and prevent evaporation at the respiratory surface.

LABORATORY EXERCISES

PURPOSE

To understand the movement of air by dissection of the respiratory tract of the fetal pig.

1. THE RESPIRATORY TRACT

This is a **two-way** path, with a single opening, which serves both as the entrance and exit for the air. Remember that the digestive tract is a one-way path and that the circulatory system is closed, with no openings.

A. The Upper Respiratory Tract

The external respiration route begins (and ends) at the **external nostrils**. Insert a blunt probe through one nostril to the **nasal cavity**. The paired cavities are separated by a **septum**, and are primarily filled with folded tissue. These folds (**conchae**) increase the surface available for <u>warming</u>, <u>cleaning</u> and <u>moistening</u> incoming air. Cut the end of the pig's snout off to get some idea of the complex structuring of the **nasal passage**. This area of the respiratory tract is also well supplied with **olfactory** nerve connections, which receive the odor stimuli.

Expose the mouth cavity by cutting through the angles of the jaw. Cut until the lower jaw can be pulled straight down. The **hard palate** which forms the roof of the mouth is the floor of the nasal cavities. Similarly, the **soft palate** divides the throat area into the dorsal nasal **pharynx** and the ventral **oral pharynx**. Locate the scoop shaped **epiglottis** at the base of the tongue. What is its function? Note the entrance to the esophagus. Gently use the blunt probe to differentiate the pathways of the respiratory tract and the digestive tract which meet in this area, the pharynx.

B.   Respiratory Organs In The Neck and Thorax

The chest cavity has already been exposed in the dissection of the circulatory system. If you have not already done so, make a mid-ventral cut in the neck region and expose the **larynx,** or voice box. You will need to carefully remove the surrounding muscles and the thyroid gland. The vocal cords are not well developed in the fetus and may not be visible when you cut open the larynx. Tracing posteriorly, expose the cartilage-braced **trachea** or windpipe until it divides into two branches, the left and right **bronchi** (singular: **bronchus**). Identify the esophagus, also present in the thoracic cavity.

Examine the lung and note that it is a multilobed structure.

C.   Density Of The Lung Tissue

Cut a piece of the lung. Note the density. How does it compare to the lung tissue of the frog? The mammalian lung consists of a great many branches and subdivisions, which serve to increase the surface area available for gas exchange. Place the piece of lung into a beaker of water and record whether it sinks or floats. What is the expected result and why? Interpret the result you actually saw in terms of the function of the lungs in the fetus and the condition of your specimen.

14

Internal Respiration-
Respiratory Function

INTRODUCTION

The lungs are the location for the interface between the respiratory tract and the circulatory system. Lung tissue is essentially a much convoluted respiratory membrane which greatly increases the surface area available for gas exchange. Lung tissue is highly **vascularized,** with many capillary networks. The blood will receive oxygen from the **inspired** air, and the **expired** air will contain carbon dioxide which has **diffused** from the blood.

There are no muscles in the lung tissue and **breathing,** the movement of air in and out of the lungs, is a mechanical process dependent on the structure and muscles of the thoracic cavity. The amount of air moving in and out of the lungs can be correlated to the **capacity** of the lungs. This serves as a measure of normal lung function and of fitness.

LABORATORY EXERCISES

PURPOSE

This exercise consists of (1) the microscopic observation of lung tissue, with a discussion of the mechanism of gas exchange and (2) measurements of lung capacity and breathing movements so as to understand the mechanism of breathing.

1. STRUCTURE OF THE LUNG

A. Cross-section of Lung Slide

Examine the slide under low power to get a general view of lung tissue within the lung. Each **bronchus** forms smaller and smaller branches (**bronchioles**) until eventually the smallest branches end in small blind pouches. (Remember, the respiratory tract is a "dead-end" path). These tiny pouches are **alveoli** (singular: **alveolus**) and are the actual site of gas exchange. Under higher magnification, look for an area where alveoli walls, usually one cell thick, can be distinguished. Look for the surrounding capillaries. ·

B. Cross-section of Human Lung with Carbon Particles

The respiratory tract not only moistens and warms the air prior to its entering the bronchioles in the lung but also cleanses it. Mucus traps foreign matter and the tracheal lining is ciliated. Nevertheless, particles do get past these defenses, as seen in this slide. Observe again the general structure of each alveolus, the supporting tissue of the lungs, **cartilage,** and the blood vessels. Why do you suppose smokers cough a lot?

2. MECHANICS OF BREATHING

A. Air Movement

Inhalation, or **inspiration** is the movement of air into the lungs. Exhalation or **expiration** is the movement of air out of the lungs. This is accomplished by changing the volume of the thoracic cavity. When the **diaphragm** and **rib muscles** contract, thoracic volume increases and air enters the lungs. When these muscles relax, thoracic volume decreases and air leaves the lungs. Observe the model demonstration of this process.

B. Lung Capacity

The **spirometer** is an instrument which measures the volume of air moving in and out of the lungs. It is used as a diagnostic tool to determine if there are any blockages or other defects reducing the normal capacity of the lungs. Conversely, trained athletes often have larger than normal lung capacity. The maximum volume of air the lungs can hold is called the **total capacity**. This is ordinarily not measurable because the normal lungs are never fully emptied (collapsed) and some air always remains in the lungs. This is about 1200 cc of air, the residual volume.

We can measure the **vital capacity** which is the maximum volume of air which can be moved in and out of the lungs. The vital capacity is the sum of three volumes: (1) **Tidal volume**, the amount of air (about 400 cc) moved in or out during a normal breath; (2) **Inspiratory reserve volume**, the amount of additional air taken in by a maximum inhalation (about 3000 cc); and (3) **Expiratory reserve volume**, the amount of additional air expired by a maximum exhalation (about 1000 cc). All these numbers are for young adult males and will vary for persons of different sizes, ages and/or sex.

The spirometers will be used to measure these volumes as follows. Prior to each measurement, be sure the spirometer is set at 0. Record the numbers in the chart.

i) Tidal volume: Rest quietly and breathe normally. When ready, pinch the nostrils to close them and exhale normally into the spirometer. Do this three times and take the average.

ii) Expiratory reserve volume (ERV): Breathe normally five times and following the last normal inhalation, exhale as much air as possible. Do this three times and record the average.

iii) Vital capacity: Breathe normally four times. At the start of the fifth breath, inhale as deeply as possible, then exhale into the spirometer as much as possible. Repeat twice, for a total of three measurements, and take the average.

TIDAL VOLUME	ERV	VITAL CAPACITY
1)		
2)		
3)		
Average: (A)	(B)	(C)

These three numbers can be used to calculate the inspiratory reserve volume (IRV), as follows:

IRV = Vital Capacity – Tidal Volume – ERV

$$IRV = \frac{\qquad}{C} - \left(\frac{\qquad}{A} + \frac{\qquad}{B} \right)$$

iv) **Effect of mild exercise.** Stand up and sit down alternately for two minutes without stopping. Immediately exhale normally into the spirometer three times, take the average and compare with the normal tidal volume. Has it increased or decreased?

C. **Breathing Movements**

The **pneumograph** is an instrument which records chest expansion and contraction. A volunteer subject will be selected for demonstration of the normal breathing movements. Note changes that occur with the following activities.

i) **Speech.** Recall the anatomy of the upper respiratory tract and the relation of speech to the movement of air.

ii) **Swallowing.** Again recall the relation between the esophagus and the glottis in the pharynx.

iii) **Exercise.** The volunteer subject should jump in place for two minutes.

iv) **Other variables.** Suggest other activites or emotional states that might result in changes in breathing movements.

15

Excretion

INTRODUCTION

Ammonia, a compound containing nitrogen, is produced by the cells of the liver as a waste product of protein metabolism. Ammonia is extremely toxic and cannot be retained by the body. In terrestrial animals, ammonia is converted by the liver into **urea** or **uric acid**, both of which are much less toxic to the body than ammonia. These substances are dissolved in the blood plasma and transported to the **kidneys**. In mammals the kidney removes the urea and other metabolic waste products and passes out **urine** which may be stored in the **bladder** for a considerable period of time before being voided.

The kidney also is important in maintaining **salt** and **water balance** as well as **acid-base balance**. Urine produced in the kidney is transported to the urinary bladder via the **ureter**. From the bladder the urine flows out the **urethra** during **micturition**, the emptying of the bladder.

The functional unit of the kidney is the **nephron**. The nephron **filters** the blood, and **reabsorbs** essential components, such as glucose, sodium, and of course **water**. The nephron consists of several regions. It begins with **Bowman's capsule**, surrounding the **glomerulus**. It continues as the **proximal convoluted tubule**, the **loop of Henle**, the **distal convoluted tubule** and the **collecting duct**.

LABORATORY EXERCISES

PURPOSE

To understand how the kidneys filter the blood and selectively excrete wastes and conserve water.

1.   THE WORK OF THE KIDNEYS

This excellent film explains the mechanism by which blood flowing through the kidney is processed, and how urine is produced by nephrons.

2.   KIDNEY STRUCTURE

The kidneys of the fetal pig will be examined as part of the dissection of the **urogenital tract**. Larger kidneys, from sheep, are to be used for studying the gross anatomy of the kidney. These kidneys are <u>hemisected</u>, to expose the various regions. Locate and identify the following regions, and label them on the kidney diagram of Figure 20.

86

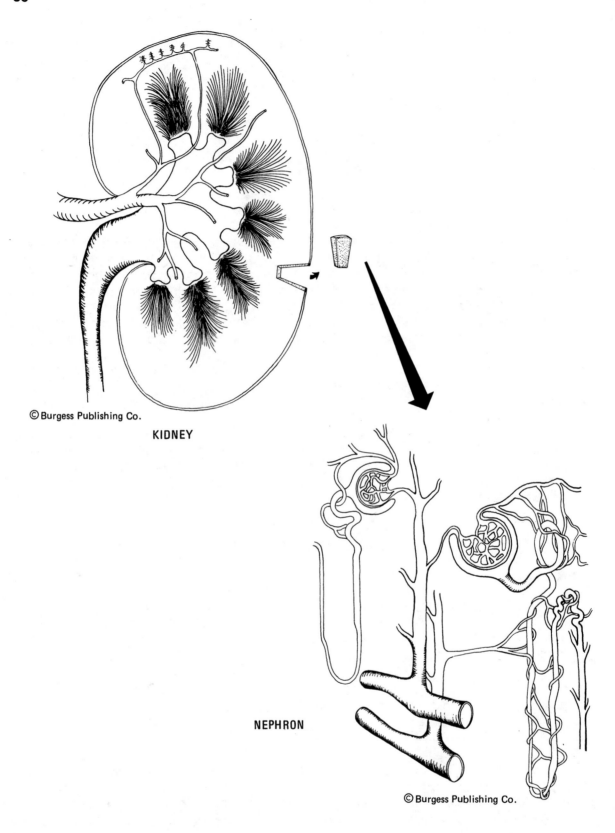

© Burgess Publishing Co.

KIDNEY

NEPHRON

© Burgess Publishing Co.

Figure 20 HUMAN NEPHRON AND KIDNEY STRUCTURE

a) **cortex.** This is the outer layer, containing the capsules and the convoluted tubules. It is distinct in appearance from the

b) **medulla** or inner layer. Which parts of the nephron are in the medulla? Note that the medulla appears divided into tufts of tissue, the **renal pyramids.** This partitioning is again visible in the organization of the

c) **pelvis.** This large chamber is divided by conical prominences which consist of the **collecting ducts** emptying urine into the **pelvic cavity.** From here the urine passes into the **ureter.** The renal artery and vein may also be visible entering and leaving the kidney.

3. CROSS–SECTION OF KIDNEY SLIDE

The miscroscopic anatomy of the kidney can be studied and further details of the structure can be seen here. First examine the entire cross–section under low power, again identifying the key divisions of the kidney. Locate a **Bowman's capsule,** which encloses the capillary tuft or **glomerulus.** Examine the **convoluted tubules** in the cortex. Locate the **collecting ducts** running parallel in the medulla. Increase the magnification and study each of these structures in detail.

Label the diagram of the **nephron** in Figure 20, and fill in the following chart.

STRUCTURE	KIDNEY LAYER	FUNCTION
Glomerulus and Bowman's capsule		
Proximal convoluted tubule		
Loop of Henle		
Distal convoluted tubule		
Collecting ducts		
Ureter		
Bladder		
Urethra		

16

Locomotion:
Skeleton & Support Tissue

INTRODUCTION

With regards to the external environment, successful adjustment behavior generally involves movements of parts of the animal or movement of the whole animal from place to place, termed **locomotion**. The forces of contraction of skeletal muscles when applied to the system of levers called the **skeleton** result in the required movements of the parts and in locomotion of the animal. The locomotor system, then, is composed of the **skeleton** and the **skeletal muscles**.

We will first study the skeletal system, and in subsequent exercises, the muscles and the systems of **coordination** and **reception** which are involved in adjustment to the environment.

The skeleton of vertebrate animals is an **endoskeleton**, a living growing organ system inside the body. This is in contradistinction to the **exoskeleton** of crustaceans and of insects, which is secreted and non-living. Since both types of the skeleton have evolved and persist, they must have survival advantages for their organisms. One advantage of the exoskeleton is superior protection. One disadvantage is a limit to body size, as the weight of an overlarge exoskeleton would crush the soft internal tissues.

The endoskeleton consists of **bones, cartilages**, and **ligaments**. While the skeleton, in the course of its evolution, has assumed many auxiliary functions, its primary role is still in locomotion. The other functions of the skeleton include **protection, support**, and from the bone **marrow**, blood cell production.

LABORATORY EXERCISES

PURPOSE

The human skeleton and the support tissues of bone and cartilage are to be studied today. The arrangement of the bones is viewed in relation to their function in locomotion. The support tissues are observed in microscopic preparations in order to understand how their composition correlates with skeletal function.

1. **GENERAL PLAN OF THE VERTEBRATE SKELETON**

Use the model of the human skeleton to identify the various parts (Figure 21).

A. <u>Axial Skeleton</u>

    1) Skull

        a) Cranial region – 8 bones

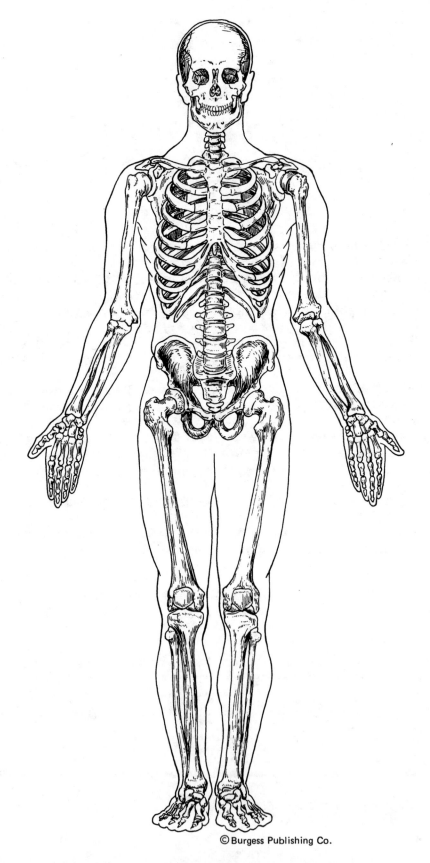

© Burgess Publishing Co.

Figure 21 HUMAN SKELETON, VENTRAL VIEW

b)   Facial region – 14 bones; ear – 6 bones

2)   Vertebral column

a)   Vertebrae – 32 bones

cervical, 7, neck

thoracic, 12, chest

lumbar, 5, abdomen

sacral, 5, hips

caudal, 3–5, tail

b)   Sternum – breast bone

c)   Ribs – 12 pairs

7 true ribs, articulating directly on sternum

3 false ribs, articulating on next higher cartilage

2 floating ribs

B.   <u>Appendicular Skeleton</u>

1)   Girdles:

	Pectoral (shoulder)	Pelvic (hip)
	scapula	ilium
	clavicle	pubis
	coracoid	ischium

2)   Appendages:

	Forelimb	Hindlimb
(upper arm)	humerus	femur (thigh)
(forearm)	radius	tibia
	ulna	fibula (shank)
(wrist)	carpals	tarsals (ankle)
(hand)	metacarpals	metatarsals (foot)
(fingers)	phalanges	phalanges (toes)

2. STRUCTURE OF THE SUPPORT TISSUES

As was indicated, the skeleton is composed mainly of three kinds of elements: **bone, cartilage,** and **ligament.** The feature common to all these tissues is that they consist of living cells dispersed in a nonliving **matrix,** or surrounding substance, secreted by the cells themselves. The matrix is of progressively decreasing order of rigidity in bone, cartilage and ligament. But since the tissue organization is easiest to comprehend in cartilage, we shall examine that first.

A. Cartilage

Obtain a prepared slide of tissue section showing cartilage. This may be a portion of a bronchus or of an ear. In either case, other tissues are associated with the cartilage, such a mucosa, fibrous tissue, smooth muscle or adipose (fat) tissue.

Locate the relatively clear band of cartilage tissue in the preparation. It consists of a dense, clear, bluish background substance in which are scattered pockets of cells arranged more or less in layers. The matrix, or intercellular substance, is a firm gel of **chondromucoid,** a glycoprotein. The **chondrocytes,** cartilage cells, lie in small cavities, **lacunae,** (singular: **lacuna**) often in groups of two or four. Surrounding the cartilage is a sheath of dense connective tissue, the **perichondrium.** In this layer may be seen blood vessels. Are there any blood vessels in the cartilage matrix? Then how are the cartilage cells supplied with food and oxygen? How would you explain that some of the lacunae have one cell and others two or four?

B. Bone

Bone is the major component of the adult vertebrate skeleton. It is not as elastic as cartilage, but much stronger in terms of resistance to **compression** and **tension.** Obtain a slide showing a section of ground bone. Only the mineralized matrix is present. No longer visible are the bone cells, the **osteocytes.** However, the spaces they were in can be seen. These are the **lacunae,** arranged in concentric layers (**lamellae**) around a central opening, the **Haversian canal.** In this canal, in the living bone, run the blood vessels and nerves to the bone cells. Since the matrix is infiltrated with impenetrable **calcium** salts, observe that the bone cells are surrounded by a radiating set of fine channels, **canaliculi,** through which oxygen and nutrients diffuse from the blood vessels. The arrangement of concentric layers around a central canal is called an **osteon** (Figure 22). Under low power, note that the section you are observing consists of several of these units. Focus on one and <u>label</u>: lacuna, canaliculi, and canal.

C. Decalcified Bone

Obtain a slide showing a section of bone from which the mineral salts of the matrix have been removed. Observe the **collagen** matrix containing the **osteocytes** in the **lacunae.** Note the **compact** and **spongy** areas. Compact bone is found toward the exterior. Around the bone may be other tissues, especially striated muscle and connective tissue.

Surrounding the bone is a fibrous cover, the **periosteum.** The innermost layer of the periosteum consists of cells which undergo division and increase the diameter of the bone.

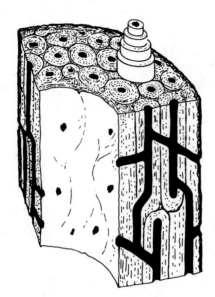

DIAGRAM OF BONE STRUCTURE

SECTION OF BONE

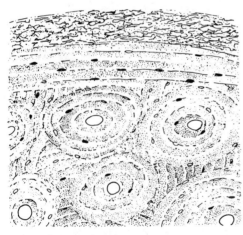

SECTION OF DRIED BONE

SECTION OF DECALCIFIED BONE

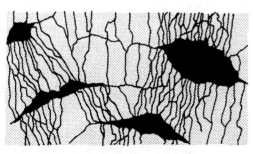

DETAILS OF OSTEON

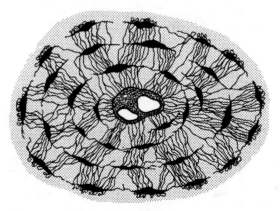

OSTEON

Figure 22 BONE, FINE STRUCTURE WITH HAVERSIAN CANAL

D. <u>Longitudinal Section of Bone</u>

Obtain a slide showing the growing end of the **femur**. The end is called the **epiphysis** (Figure 23). Note again the orientation of the **spongy** and **compact** areas. Note also the **marrow**. The marrow is found in the **medullary cavity** and is the area of blood cell production.

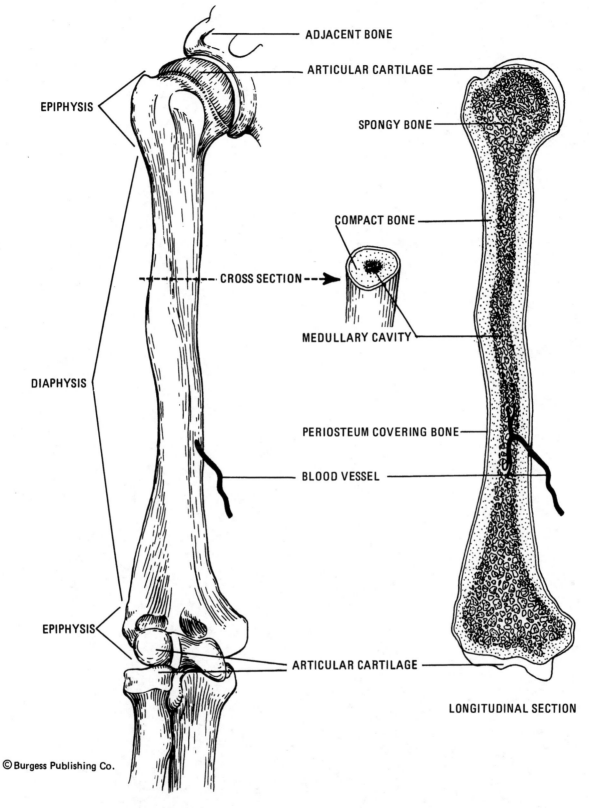

ADJACENT BONE

ARTICULAR CARTILAGE

SPONGY BONE

EPIPHYSIS

COMPACT BONE

CROSS SECTION

DIAPHYSIS

MEDULLARY CAVITY

PERIOSTEUM COVERING BONE

BLOOD VESSEL

EPIPHYSIS

ARTICULAR CARTILAGE

LONGITUDINAL SECTION

© Burgess Publishing Co.

EXTERNAL APPEARANCE

Figure 23 BONE, GROSS STRUCTURE OF LONG BONE

17

Locomotion: Joints and Muscles

INTRODUCTION

Locomotion or movement of a limb is due to the activity of muscles attached to bones. **Joints** are regions where bones meet, or **articulate**.

The **articulations** are designed for different degrees of movement ranging from none to movement in any direction.

Muscles are able to produce movements depending upon the nature of the joint and the places of attachment of the muscles.

A muscle can perform work by **contraction** (shortening). In its shortened condition, it can either remain contracted or relaxed. It can do **no work** when being stretched. Most muscles are, therefore, arranged in **antagonistic pairs**, one member of a pair producing motion in one direction, its antagonist producing motion in the opposite direction.

Skeletal muscle is the name given to the muscle concerned in locomotion. This muscle is under **voluntary** nervous control and is striped or **striated** in appearance. The bulk of body weight is due to skeletal muscle.

Smooth muscle is under **involuntary** nervous control and is found in the internal organs, such as those of the intestinal tract.

Cardiac muscle is **involuntary** and is found in the heart.

All three kinds of muscles owe their contractibility to the proteins **Actin** and **Myosin**. The energy for contraction is provided by **ATP** and the **calcium** ion is also required. The differences in appearance are caused by the differences in arrangement of the protein **filaments** or **myofibrils** within the muscle cells. Note that all three types are under nervous control.

LABORATORY EXERCISES

PURPOSE

The different kinds of joints, the three kinds of muscle tissue and the interaction of skeletal muscle and joint articulation for locomotion will be studied. The microscopic appearance of muscle tissue will be correlated to the mechanism of contraction.

1. TYPES OF JOINTS

Use the models of the human skeleton to identify the following joints:

a) **Sutures** are immovable joints, such as those between the bones of the cranium which are firmly fastened together by dense connective tissue.

b) **Compressible joints** occur between the vertebrae. The intervertebral cartilage disks are fluid-filled and may be compressed by the bending movements of the body.

c) **Gliding joints** are found in the wrist. The bones are held together tightly by fastening ligaments that permit only slight movement.

d) **Hinge joints** in the fingers, toes, and knees permit considerably more movement, but only in one plane.

e) The **pivot joint** at the elbow permits not only hinge movement of the forearm but also rotation of the hand. The articulation of radius and ulna to the humerus is such as to permit circling of the radius around the ulna near the wrist.

f) The **ball-and-socket joint** permits the greatest range of movement, especially in locomotion. It is found where the head of the femur fits into the acetabulum of the pelvis, and also between the humerus and scapula.

2. OPERATION OF SKELETON AND MUSCLE

A preserved frog will be used to demonstrate the work of **antagonistic** muscle pairs. Note the following muscles of the hind limb:

a) **Triceps femoris** - a very large, broad muscle covering the anterior face of the thigh.

b) **Gracilis major** - on the inner half of the posterior surface of the thigh.

c) **Semi-membranosus** - on the outer half of the posterior surface of the thigh.

d) **Gastrocnemius** - the calf muscle.

e) **Tibialis anticus** - the muscle lying on the anterior surface of the shank bone.

Each of these muscles is attached to the bones so that it **spans two joints**. Identify the joints involved for each muscle and the bones to which each is attached. Sketch the position of the muscles on Figure 24. (The gastrocnemius muscle has already been drawn in as an example). From your knowledge of the action of muscles, fill in the following chart.

(A movement which causes a limb to bend at a joint is called **flexion**; one which causes the limb to straighten is called **extension**).

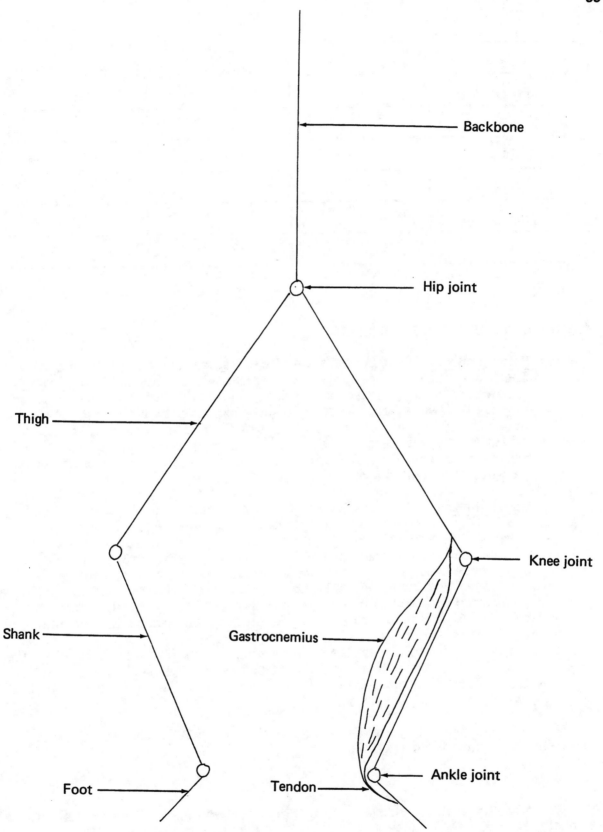

Figure 24 JOINT ARTICULATION

MUSCLE	AT HIP JOINT	ACTION AT KNEE JOINT	AT ANKLE JOINT
triceps femoris			
gracilis major			
semi-membranosus			
gastrocnemius			
tibialis anticus			

3. STRUCTURE OF MUSCLE TISSUE

a) Smooth muscle. Examine the slide of a cross-section of the small intestine. The finger-like structures of the villi project into the lumen. Under low power the two muscle layers, circular and longitudinal, are visible on the periphery. Identify the two layers. Under high power examine the circular layer in order to see the appearance of the muscle cells (Figure 25). Note that each cell contains a nucleus. Not visible are the myofibrils in the cytoplasm. These two muscle layers are antagonistic to each other and their contractions result in peristalsis. Smooth muscle is not easily fatigued.

b) Striated muscle. Examine the slide showing a section of skeletal muscle. Skeletal muscle contractions are stronger than smooth, but this muscle tires more easily. Note the organization of this tissue into fibers. Identify the nuclei and observe the absence of individual cells (Figure 25). The striped appearance is due to the arrangement of the actin and myosin protein filaments. The filaments are arranged in units, called sarcomeres, which have alternating light and dark bands (Figure 26). As the myofibrils of each muscle cell are all parallel and very closely aligned, a striped appearance results.

c) Cardiac muscle. Examine the slide showing muscle from the heart. Note the structural arrangement, intermediate between smooth and striated muscle. This reflects the properties of cardiac muscle, which does not tire easily but is capable of rapid contraction.

Review the appearance of all three muscle types (Figure 25) in relation to the requirements of each type.

4. MUSCLE FATIGUE

As noted above, skeletal muscle is capable of performing rapid contractions but it is easily fatigued. The ergometer will be used to demonstrate this property. A male and a female volunteer should be compared to determine if there is any difference in the properties of the muscles of the two sexes.

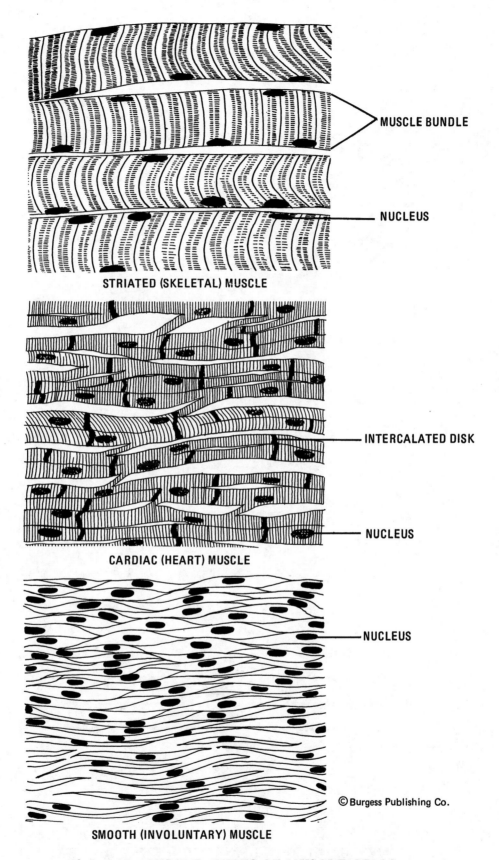

MUSCLE BUNDLE

NUCLEUS

STRIATED (SKELETAL) MUSCLE

INTERCALATED DISK

NUCLEUS

CARDIAC (HEART) MUSCLE

NUCLEUS

© Burgess Publishing Co.

SMOOTH (INVOLUNTARY) MUSCLE

Figure 25 . MUSCLE, TYPES OF MUSCLE CELLS

102

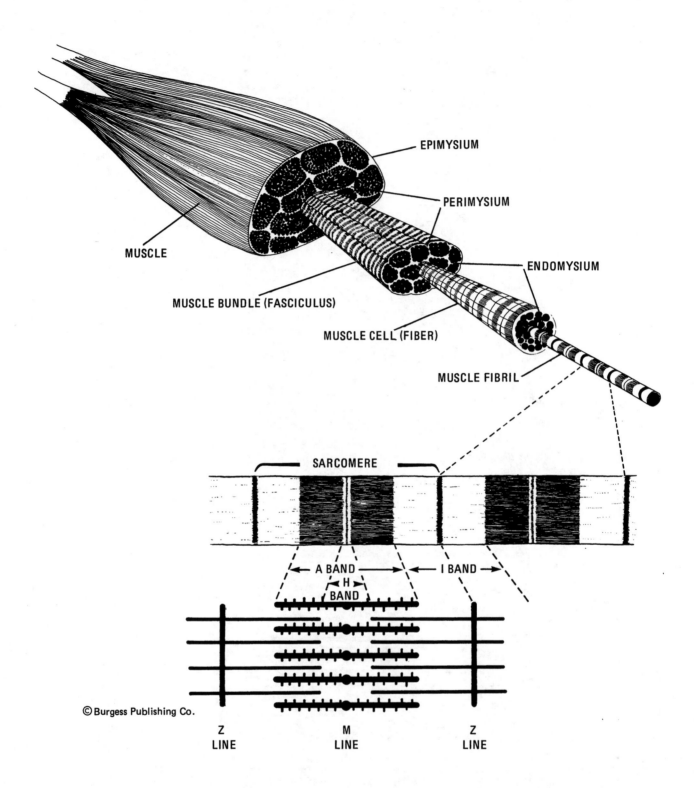

EPIMYSIUM

PERIMYSIUM

MUSCLE

ENDOMYSIUM

MUSCLE BUNDLE (FASCICULUS)

MUSCLE CELL (FIBER)

MUSCLE FIBRIL

SARCOMERE

A BAND

H
BAND

I BAND

© Burgess Publishing Co.

Z
LINE

M
LINE

Z
LINE

Figure 26 MUSCLE, SHOWING FINE STRUCTURE OF A SARCOMERE

18

Coordination-
The Endocrines

INTRODUCTION

The multiple functions of the body are synchronized and regulated by two basic control systems: **Endocrine** (chemical) and **Neural** (electrochemical). The systems are interdependent, as the neural system has chemical components and the endocrines are subject to neural control. Together they serve to integrate and control the functions of the various organ systems we have studied up to this point. They are particularly important for the organism in **homeostasis**, that is in the maintenance of the constancy of the internal environment.

Neural control is characterized by rapid, precise and often localized action. A neural reaction is quick and of short duration. Endocrine control is, by contrast, slower but more sustained.

The endocrine glands secrete **hormones** which have profound effects on metabolism, growth, reproduction and, to some extent, behavior. All of the glands are extensively **vascularized;** their products are picked up by capillaries in the glandular tissues and then transported by the blood stream all over the body.

A hormone that affects a given tissue or tissues may remain in the blood stream throughout life, even being carefully regulated by **feedback systems** so that its presence in the body is kept at a given level more or less forever. Some hormones have very definite **target tissues** which they influence despite the fact that the hormones pass many other tissues with no reaction. Other hormones have a **general effect** over most of the tissues in the body.

LABORATORY EXERCISES

PURPOSE

We will study the important endocrine glands and discuss the chemical control of the body. The materials used are four prepared slides showing sections of (1) the pituitary (entire hypophysis), (2) the thyroid (and parathyroids), (3) the adrenal glands and (4) the pancreas. These are not the only endocrine glands. For example, we have not yet noted the hormonal secretions of the gonads. The glands studied will illustrate the general nature of endocrine control.

1.   THE PITUITARY GLAND

Take a stained slide that shows the entire pituitary gland. It will have to be from a small mammal since the human pituitary is much too large for one slide. The pituitary is sometimes called the **hypophysis** and is located in a most important site just below the **hypothalamus** of the brain.

104

Many hormones originate in the pituitary gland. The most notable are the **tropic** hormones, which have for their target tissues other endocrine glands.

Begin by finding the major sections of the gland. First locate the **neurohypophysis**, which passes downward from the hypothalamus of the brain. Its appearance is similar to the hypothalamus because it too is composed of nerve tissue. The anterior part is called the **adenohypophysis**. It is composed of glandular epithelium interspersed with delicate connective tissues and blood vessels. The pituitary is attached to the hypothalamus by the **infundibular stalk**. Near to this stalk is an area of the gland filled with blood vessels. The entire gland is covered with a **capsule**. Between the adenohypophysis and the neurohypophysis is a poorly defined intermediate area. In mammals the anterior and posterior lobes are closely meshed. The adenohypophysis secretes a number of hormones made of protein. The most important of these are the tropic hormones. To distinguish between the terms tropic and trophic, remember that tropic means "to turn" while trophic means "to grow." These words are used carelessly sometimes, but true tropic hormones are those coming from the pituitary that influence other endocrine glands.

The pituitary gland has a **feed-back** relationship with these glands. The tropic hormone stimulates the **target** gland and the hormone from the target gland inhibits areas of the hypothalamus which control the pituitary. These hypothalamic regions produce **releasing factors**—small hormone-like molecules—which are carried by a special group of blood vessels—**hypophyseal portal circulatory system**—directly to the adenohypophysis. When they arrive, the releasing factors allow the tropic hormones to leave the pituitary cells and enter the blood stream (Figure 27).

The tropic hormones of the adenohypophysis are: (1) **TSH**, the thyroid-stimulating hormone; (2) **FSH**, the follicle-stimulating hormone; (3) **LH**, the luteinizing hormone; and (4) **ACTH**, the adrenal cortical tropic hormone. Two other hormones from this tissue are not precisely tropic but are sometimes considered so. One is **prolactin**, which stimulates the production of milk by mammary glands. The other is **STH**, the somatotrophic hormone or "growth hormone." Thus, there are a total of six hormones produced.

The target tissues for these hormones are as follows: TSH to the thyroid gland, FSH to the follicle in the ovary, LH to the corpus luteum in the ovary, ACTH to the adrenal cortex, prolactin to the mammary glands and STH to the epiphyseal cartilages of the bones. FSH and LH also affect the testes of the male, FSH going to the seminiferous tubules and LH stimulating the interstitial secretory cells. Another name for LH in the male is ICSH, which indicates the target tissue involved.

There are other effects such as the "mothering instinct" promoted by prolactin and some metabolic effect on muscle and fat by STH. Overproduction (**hypersecretion**) of STH in infancy leads to gigantism. **Undersecretion** has the opposite effect (midgets).

The **neurohypophysis** stores and releases two hormones which are actually produced in the brain, in the hypothalamus. **Oxytocin** has for its target tissue the myometrium (smooth muscle) of the uterus, causing it to contract. **Vasopressin** (ADH) influences the kidney tubule, promoting the reabsorption of water. Water is taken back into the blood from the kidney. This hormone thus has an **antidiuretic effect**, decreasing the volume of urine.

Draw the entire pituitary gland and label:

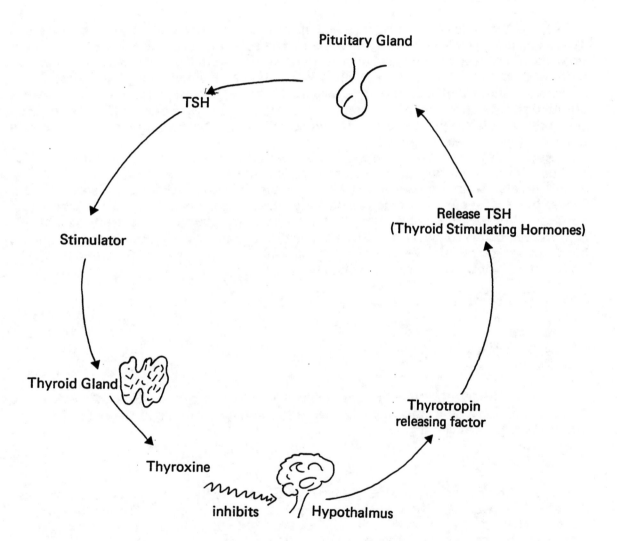

Figure 27 A NEGATIVE FEEDBACK CONTROL LOOP

capsule

hypothalamus

neurohypophysis

adenohypophysis

infundibular stalk

2. THYROID GLAND, PARATHYROIDS

Place the slide of the thyroid gland on your microscope stage and look for **follicles**. These circular, single-celled layers are actually spherical and enclose a **colloid** which consists of several proteins, some of which contain **thyroxine**, plus some enzymes. It is a dense colloidal solution that usually takes a stain and which might have some shrinkage spaces that look like clear bubbles. The follicle cells secrete thyroxine when stimulated by TSH from the pituitary. Thyroxine regulates the **basal metabolic** rate of the body and also inhibits the hypothalamus so that the thyroxine level in the blood is more or less constant (Figure 27).

Normal levels of thyroxine are needed as well during development. In frogs the metamorphosis from tadpole to adult forms is controlled by thyroxine and will not occur at low levels. If absent in humans, a form of mental retardation, **cretinism**, will occur. In adults insufficient thyroxine is called **myxedema** and is characterized by obesity, dullness, slurred speech and slowed heart rate. If the thyroid levels are too high (**hyperthyroidism**), there is weight loss, constant appetite, body tremor and fast heart beat. Bulging eyeballs are often present as well but this symptom is caused by the high TSH levels—not by the high thyroxine levels.

Draw a portion of the thyroid gland and label:

colloid
blood vessels
follicle

Locate the parathyroid glands which produce **parathormone**. They are embedded in the thyroid gland. Parathormone increases the level of calcium in the blood by stimulating its release from bone.

3. ADRENAL GLAND

Examine the prepared slide of the **adrenal gland**. Find the **capsule** which encloses the gland. Locate the **cortex**, which is the thick outer tissue, and the **medulla** or center. It should be noted that the two parts of the adrenal gland are actually two different endocrine glands or at least two different endocrine tissues.

The **cortex**, which is stimulated by the pituitary's ACTH, has three zones. The outer zone, next to the capsule, is the **zona glomerulosa**. It is a thin layer with cells closely packed and arranged in clumps, short columns or even arcs. The thicker central zone of the cortex is the **zona fasciculata**, so named for its fasciculate appearance. Fascicles (bundles) of long columns of cortex cells are seen. The **zona reticularis** is adjacent to the medulla, with its cells arranged in a netlike fashion. However, these three zones are not clearly marked. The cells merge from zone to zone gradually. The best way to immediately establish a distinction between cortex and medulla is to view the slide on low-power or scanning lens. As your magnification increases, the overall distinctions become blurred. The cortex secretes the cortical hormones, which are steroids and have a number of important functions. There are three main groups of **corticosteroids**: (1) **glucocorticoids**, involved in regulating carbohydrate balance and fat and protein metabolism; (2) **mineralcorticoids**, concerned with salt balance; and (3) **androgens** that affect the sexual activities of the body.

The **medulla** has an irregular boundary with the **zona reticularis**. The medullary cells are arranged in irregular groups with many blood vessels separating them. The medulla is neural in origin. Look for nerve cells. These are **sympathetic ganglion cells**. The medulla secretes **epinephrine (adrenalin)** and **norepinephrine**. Much more epinephrine is secreted and this is one of the hormones with a behavioral effect. It arouses the body for physical activity while it depresses visceral activity. Norepinephrine has an effect that is similar to epinephrine but is more active. Norepinephrine also stimulates the pineal gland to make the hormone melatonin, and acts as a neurotransmitter in the brain.

Draw the entire adrenal gland and label:

capsule	zona glomerulosa
cortex	zona fasciculata
medulla	zona reticularis
sympathetic nerve cell	blood vessel

4. PANCREAS

Examine the slide that shows a section through the pancreas. Begin by finding the little tubules (**acini**) that secrete and transport the pancreatic juice toward the pancreatic duct. These innumerable tubules or lobules of the **exocrine** (secreting into duct) part of the pancreas form the greatest part of the section. You will also see blood vessels which serve both parts of the gland. The endocrine part of the gland consists of round clusters of lightly staining cells which do not have a lumen like the acinus. These are the **islets of Langerhans**, which secrete the two hormones that regulate sugar balance in the body fluids. The **alpha** (A) cells secrete the hormone **glucagon**, the **beta** cells (B) secrete **insulin**. Glucagon increases blood glucose levels. Insulin decreases blood glucose levels by stimulating glucose entry into cells. **Diabetes mellitus** is a disease characterized by high levels of blood glucose.

Draw a section of the pancreas and label:

islet of Langerhans
acinus (exocrine structure)
blood vessels

19

Coordination-
Neural

INTRODUCTION

Neural coordination involves rapid, short-lived responses. The cells of the nervous system are **neurons**, along which the nervous **impulse** travels. Neural pathways are precise and involve the following elements:

1) **Receptors** receive and collect information. This information is transmitted along **sensory** neurons, so called because some (not all) receptors involve sense organs. They carry information <u>towards</u> the place where the information is processed and are, therefore, also referred to as **afferent** neurons.

2) The **Central Nervous System** (CNS), consists of the **brain** and **spinal cord**. The CNS processes and stores (memory) the information received from **afferent** neurons.

3) **Effectors** act upon the information received from the CNS. Impulses <u>leaving</u> the CNS are carried along **efferent** (<u>away</u> <u>from</u>) neurons. These neurons are also referred to as **motor** neurons because the effector is often a muscle.

In sum, neural pathways travel from **receptors** via neurons (**conductors**) to **effectors**. A nerve-effector reaction is quick and of short duration. This is due to the electro-chemical nature of the nerve impulse.

The behavior shown by an animal when a given receptor is stimulated is determined by the particular nerve pathways communicating between the receptor and effector. Some involuntary behavior patterns involve only the receptor, a sensory neuron, an adjustor neuron in the spinal cord, and a motor neuron to the effector. Such a pathway is called a **reflex arc** and the behavior pattern involved is called a simple reflex action. More complex reflex arcs may also involve neurons in the brain. Even more complex brain functions, such as memory, are little understood.

LABORATORY EXERCISE

PURPOSE

We will examine the structure of the brain and the spinal cord, and observe reflex action. The anatomy of the CNS is correlated with the various integrating and regulating functions of the nervous system.

1. STRUCTURE OF THE BRAIN

Obtain a whole and a hemisected sheep's brain. Examine the dorsal surface of the whole brain (Figure 28), and identify the **cerebrum**. In human brains, this is the largest area, concerned with memory, thought and learning. The surface of the cerebrum, the **cerebral cortex** of gray matter is folded. Note that the cerebrum is divided into left and right **hemispheres**. Just posterior to the cerebrum is the **cerebellum**. It also has a folded cortex and is the area of the brain which coordinates muscular activity.

On the ventral surface (Figure 29), locate the **medulla** and the **pons**. The medulla regulates the rates of heart beat and breathing, as well as blood pressure. The pons (= bridge) connects the cerebellum with other parts of the brain and with the spinal cord. Note the **optic chiasma** formed by the crossing of the optic nerves. The other cranial nerves, shown on Figure 29 are probably missing from your specimen. The specimen you are observing may also be missing the membranes which normally cover the brain, the **meninges.**

On the hemisected brain (Figure 30), find the **corpus callosum**, a band of white matter consisting of fibers which connect the two cerebral hemispheres. Note the pair of prominences covered over by the cerebral hemispheres; the anterior one is a visual correlation center, the posterior one is an auditory correlation center.

The **forebrain** consists of the cerebral cortex, which you have already identified, and the **thalamus** and **hypothalamus** regions. Locate these latter two regions on the hemisected brain. The thalamus receives all the sensory nerves except the olfactory nerves. The hypothalamus is a key area of the brain for the maintenance of **homeostasis** in processes such as body temperature and water balance. In addition, releasing factors and hormones affecting pituitary activity are produced here. The pituitary gland itself is seen as an oval structure ventral to the hypothalamus. This area thus constitutes an important connection between the two modes of coordination: neural and endocrine.

The **midbrain** is relatively unimportant in mammals, and consists primarily of fiber bundles joining the cortex to the rest of the brain.

The **hindbrain** consists of structures already seen: The cerebellum, the pons and the medulla. The **stem** of the hindbrain continues as the spinal cord. Label all of the brain areas on Figures 28, 29, and 30.

2. STRUCTURE OF THE SPINAL CORD

The spinal cord is the second component of the CNS.

Study the slide showing a cross-section of the spinal cord of a vertebrate. Examine the specimen first under scan. Note the H-shaped central area; this is the "gray matter" of the spinal cord and consists of both nerve fibers and cell bodies. Remember that collections of neurons constitute nerve fibers. The outer area of "white matter" consists of fibers going toward or coming from the brain. The white color in the living spinal cord is due to the presence of **myelin** in the sheaths of these fibers.

Examine the specimen with your low power objective. Note the large cells ventrally located in the "gray matter." These are the cell bodies of **motor neurons.** The cell bodies of **adjustor** (internuncial) **neurons** may also be seen in the "gray matter." Those of the **sensory neurons** are located in the **ganglia** (singular = ganglion) of the dorsal roots of the spinal nerves.

Examine Figure 31 for impulse pathways in the spinal cord.

Note that the cell **body** of the neuron is always within the CNS. The length of many nerve fibers is due to the special structure of neurons, especially the projections from the cell body. The components of the neuron, and the structural differences between sensory and motor neurons are diagrammed in Figure 32.

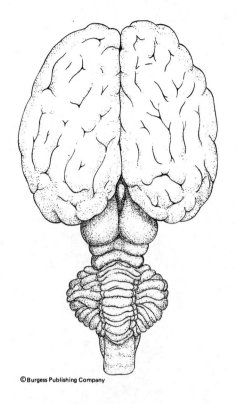

©Burgess Publishing Company

Figure 28 SHEEP BRAIN, DORSAL VIEW

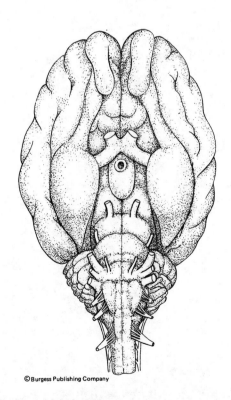

©Burgess Publishing Company

Figure 29 SHEEP BRAIN, VENTRAL VIEW

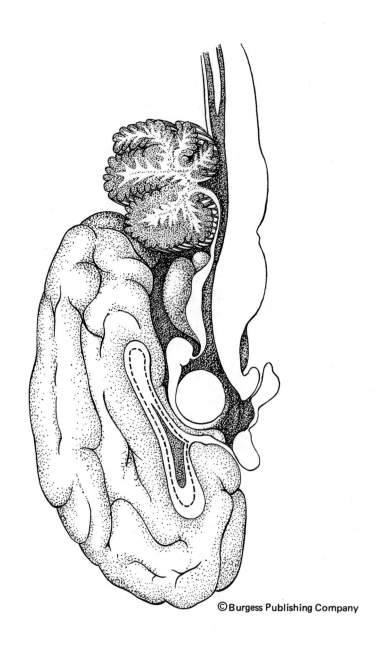

Figure 30 SHEEP BRAIN, MIDSAGITTAL SECTION

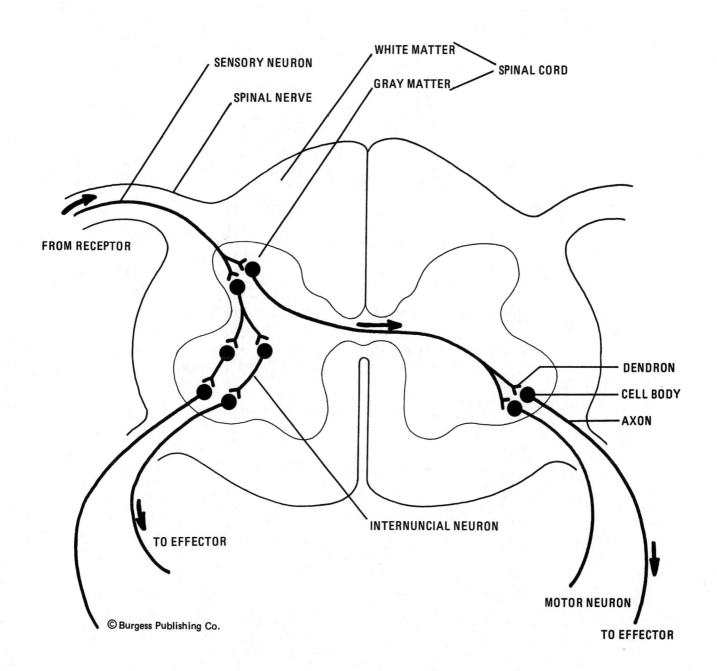

SENSORY NEURON

WHITE MATTER

SPINAL CORD

SPINAL NERVE

GRAY MATTER

FROM RECEPTOR

DENDRON

CELL BODY

AXON

TO EFFECTOR

INTERNUNCIAL NEURON

© Burgess Publishing Co.

MOTOR NEURON

TO EFFECTOR

Figure 31 NERVE TISSUE, DIAGRAM OF REFLEX ARC

114

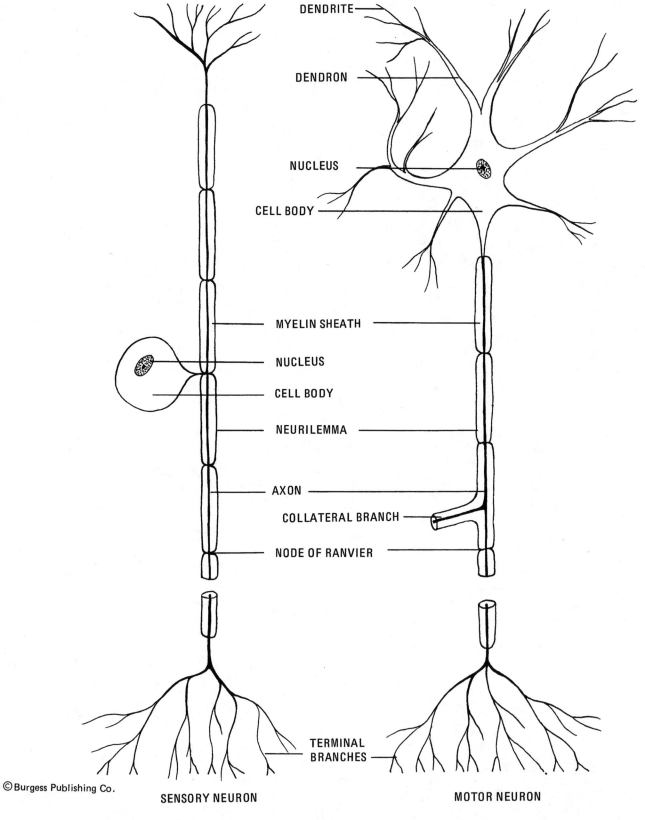

DENDRITE

DENDRON

NUCLEUS

CELL BODY

MYELIN SHEATH

NUCLEUS

CELL BODY

NEURILEMMA

AXON

COLLATERAL BRANCH

NODE OF RANVIER

TERMINAL BRANCHES

SENSORY NEURON

MOTOR NEURON

Figure 32 NERVE TISSUE, DIAGRAM OF MOTOR AND SENSORY NEURON

3. REFLEXES IN MAN

A. Knee Jerk

Sit on the edge of the table with your legs dangling and let your teammate tap your patella tendon just below the knee cap with a rubber hammer. Describe what happens. Repeat the procedure while attempting to inhibit the response by force of will. What is the effect? Repeat once more; this time clench both fists tightly before the tendon is struck. Does this make any difference?

B. Pupillary Reflex

Close your eyes. When you open them, your teammate will shine a light into your left eye. Does the size of the pupil change when the light strikes the eye? Repeat the procedure, this time looking at the pupil of the right eye when the left eye is illuminated. Does light on one eye affect the pupil of the other, or not? Explain.

Watch the subject's pupils when he looks at: (1) an object one foot away, and (2) a distant object. Is there any difference?

20

Sensory Reception

INTRODUCTION

Animals receive information concerning their environment via neural **receptors**. The central nervous system coordinates and **translates** this information and stimulates the appropriate **effectors**. Sensory receptors may range from nerve endings scattered on the surface to complex organs consisting of a concentration of a particular type of receptor. Such specialized organs are **sense organs** such as the eye, or the ear. In all cases, the receptors are modified neurons sensitive to a particular stimulus. The stimulus initiates an impulse which travels to the brain, where it is properly interpreted, or translated. Not all sensory receptors produce conscious sensations. There are receptors in various internal body organs which enable the brain to coordinate their proper functioning.

The skin contains separate receptors to cold, heat, pain, and pressure as well as to touch. In the tongue, the taste buds are an example of a simple type of receptor; olfactory neurons are present in the nose. Taste and smell together determine our response to food. The eye and the ear are more complex types of receptors. The eye responds to light, the ear to sound waves. Thus the sense receptors enable us to interpret and respond to both our internal and external environments.

LABORATORY EXERCISES

PURPOSE

The best known senses are the ones we are most familiar with: sight, hearing, smell, taste, and touch. We will do exercises on the functioning of our own sense organs so as to understand the nature of sensory reception. The structure of one sense organ, the eye, will be examined in a dissection.

1. STRUCTURE OF THE EYE

Obtain a hemisected sheep's eye. Examine the posterior portion of the eye and locate the optic nerve. Note that the posterior wall of the eye is composed of three layers: the external, white **sclera**; the black middle layer, the **choroid**; and the inner layer, the **retina**. The retina contains special light sensitive cells, the **rods** and **cones**. In the preserved eye, the retina appears to be separated from the choroid layer. In life, it is closely applied to the choroid. Note the central **blind spot** where the optic nerve joins the retina.

The portion of the sclera which covers the front of the eye is transparent (when alive) and is called the **cornea**. Examine the front of the eye. Going posteriorly from the cornea, find the **iris** and the **pupil** and the **lens**.

118

2. CHARACTERISTICS OF RECEPTORS

A. The Eye

Test your own vision by the following methods:

1) Use the standard eye-test chart for visual acuity;

2) Use the book of colored illustrations to test for color blindness.

3) 2-dot discrimination.

Visual acuity is the ability to recognize two adjacent objects as being distinct from each other. This is essentially what is being measured by the standard eye-test chart. On a white card make two black dots about the size of periods exactly one millimeter apart. Measure and record the greatest distance at which you can identify the dots as being separate.

record visual acuity:
Maximum distance of 2-dot discrimination _____

4) Visual accommodation: The eye does not simultaneously focus on both near and distant objects. Face the window. Close and relax your eyes for a few moments while your teammate places his hand, with fingers spread, about six or eight inches from your eyes. Then open your eyes without any attempt to focus. Which is in clear focus, the building across the street or your teammate's fingers? Is the relaxed eye focused for close or distance vision? What is presbyopia?

5) Depth perception: Use the lighted box containing two sticks connected to a string. Pull on the string until you believe the two sticks are next to each other, using only one eye. Repeat using both eyes. Repeat the adjustment by having your teammate move the two sticks at varying distances from each other before you try to line them up correctly.

depth perception:

NUMBERS OF ERRORS IN TEN TRIALS	
with both eyes	with one eye

6) Blind spot: On a sheet of paper draw a black circle about $\frac{1}{4}$ to $\frac{1}{2}$ inch in diameter. About four inches to the right of the circle, draw a heavy black cross of about the same size. Hold the sheet 20 inches away from your face and cover your left eye with your free hand. Direct your gaze on the circle and slowly move the paper closer. At a certain distance, the cross will disappear from view. Where on your retina is the image of the cross located at this time?

B. <u>The Ear</u>

1) Sound localization: The ability to recognize the direction of a sound depends in part on the relative intensity of the sound in the two ears. Close your eyes while your teammate clicks together a pair of coins. He will move after each click so as to occupy different positions. Each of his positions will be just beyond your arm's reach. After each click, point in the direction from which the sound seems to come. Your teammate will record the degree of error. Repeat with one ear stopped by a finger.

<u>sound</u> <u>localization</u>:

AVERAGE ERROR	
with both ears	with one ear

2) Fatigue of sound receptors: Different frequencies of musical tone are detected by different nerve endings. A continual sound of unvarying pitch rapidly fatigues these nerve endings. Sound a tuning fork at the bell of a stethoscope used in the normal way but with one of the tubes pinched shut by a clamp. While the fork is still sounding release the pinched tube and notice the difference in sound in the two ears.

3) Hearing by bone conduction: When you hear your own voice as you speak, only some of the sound is transmitted through the action of the ear drum. Some of the sound is carried by the bones of the skull. Close both your ears, while your teammate sounds a tuning fork first in the air near your head, and then with the stem touching your teeth.

C. <u>Taste Localization</u>

Obtain five applicators. Dip one applicator into a 5% sucrose solution and then touch the following regions of your tongue with the moistened applicator:

1) Tip
2) Front side edge
3) Upper front center
4) Upper back center
5) Back side edge
6) Lower center

Record where a sweet sensation is most distinct (++++), less distinct (++), or is not registered at all. Rinse your mouth.

Using separate applicators, repeat the above test with each of the following solutions in the order given: 10% NaCl, 1% acetic acid, 0.001% of quinine, and phenyl thiocarbamide (PTC) solution. Rinse your mouth after each series of tests. Record for salty, sour and bitter sensations.

	Sugar	Salt	Acid	Quinine	PTC
Tip					
Front Side Edge					
Upper Front Center					
Upper Back Center					
Back Side Edge					
Lower Center					

D. Touch Localization

The nerve endings which are sensitive to a light touch are more numerous on some parts of the skin than on others. Close your eyes while your teammate touches the back of your hand with both tips of a pair of forceps. Measure the smallest distance between the divider tips that will give the sensation of two separate stimuli.

Repeat the test on the palm, finger tip, lip, and inner wrist surface.

MINIMUM DISTANCE OF 2-POINT DISCRIMINATION				
back of hand	palm	finger tip	lip	wrist

E. Temperature Discrimination

Prepare three beakers of water: one hot, one at room temperature, one of iced water. Simultaneously dip the left forefinger into the hot water and the right forefinger into the cold water. Hold them there for ten seconds. Then put both fingers into the beaker of water at room temperature. Compare the sensation in the two fingers. Using different fingers, repeat the experiment, this time following the initial dip by placing both fingers in the hot water. Repeat once more, this time placing both fingers in the cold water after the initial dip.

Cold and heat affect different receptors in the skin. In this experiment, one set of receptors become fatigued by the initial stimulation while the other set remain unaffected.

	Left Hand (from hot water)	Right Hand (from cold water)
Water at room temperature		
Hot Water		
Cold Water		

F. Kinesthetic Sense

Close your eyes, raise your hands to shoulder level and extend your forefingers. With your eyes closed, attempt to make the tips of the forefingers meet in front of you. How did you "know" where your fingers were? Are all sensory receptors concerned with external stimulation?

21

Excretory and Reproductive Systems- Dissection of the Fetal Pig

INTRODUCTION

Reproduction is, as the name implies, a process of making anew a facsimile of an existing item. Biological reproduction is the making of a new organism by an existing organism. Such self-replacement is one of the key characteristics of living things. Some organisms reproduce **asexually**, or **vegetatively**. This results in identity between parent and offspring. **Sexual** reproduction requires the participation of two organisms, and the offspring are similar, but not identical to the parents. We will cover the genetic and evolutionary consequences of sexual reproduction later, but it should be noted now that the variability in offsprings is a consequence of the prevalence of sexual reproduction among most biological species.

In mammals (and most sexually reproducing organisms), each generation begins with the union of two specialized cells or **gametes**, the **sperm** and **egg**. The fusion of the sperm and egg nuclei is **fertilization**. The result is a **zygote** which will develop into the new organism.

In mammals, fertilization and development are internal, and the reproductive system is designed to place the gametes in proximity for fertilization, and to support development in the **uterus** of the female. These processes are, therefore, preceded by **copulation** and **insemination**. Gametes are produced in the **gonads**: **testes** in the male and **ovaries** in the female. The gonads also secrete **hormones** which regulate reproductive functions.

Anatomically, the excretory and reproductive systems of vertebrates in general, and mammals specifically, are in close association. Therefore, the dissection of the two systems can be done together.

LABORATORY EXERCISES

PURPOSE

To dissect the urogenital system of the fetal pig; to compare the male and female systems; to understand the functioning of the parts of the reproductive tract.

1. ARRANGEMENT OF EXCRETORY ORGANS

You have already located the kidney during your dissection of the circulatory system. Expose the left **kidney** by peeling the peritoneal membrane from its ventral surface. Find the origin of the **ureter**, the tube which carries urine from the kidney to the bladder. As it approaches the bladder, the ureter is adjacent to some of the reproductive organs. Care must be taken not to destroy these structures. Examine the urinary **bladder** which is located between the two umbilical arteries. Note that it extends posteriorly and dorsally into the region of the pelvic girdle. We will follow the

urethra, which carries urine from the bladder to the exterior during the dissection of the reproductive system. You will dissect only one sex, but you must observe both male and female pigs.

2. FEMALE GENITAL SYSTEM

Pass a probe between the urinary bladder and the flap of the abdominal wall which still has the umbilical cord attached to it. Free the ventral surface of the bladder from the abdominal wall flap by tearing the membrane. Using your scissors, cut across the wall flap. Place the bladder in the body cavity so that it rests against the visceral organs. Note that the **urethra** disappears posteriorly into the pelvic region. In order to expose the urethra and some of the female genital organs, the ventral portion of the **pelvic girdle** must be cut. Using your scissors, cut through the body wall along the ventral midline from the abdominal wall flap almost to the papilla. Insert the point of the scissors into the space occupied by the urethra and cut through the pelvic girdle. Be sure that you are cutting ventral to the urethra. When the cut is completed, spread the hindlimbs of the pig by tightening the cords.

Use your forceps to clear the membranes away.

Follow the urethra to the point at which it joins the tube lying directly dorsal to itself.

The second tube can be more clearly seen if the bladder is once again placed outside of the body cavity so that the urethra is pulled to the side.

The second tube consists of the **vagina** and anterior to the vagina, the **common uterus**. The common uterus extends anteriorly for a short distance and then divides into two **uterine horns**. The horns are short in the fetus and are continuous with the **oviducts**. The oviducts and uterine horns are attached to the body wall by a broad ligament. The funnel-shaped openings of the oviducts are closely applied to the small oval **ovaries**.

Locate the **rectum** which lies dorsal to the vagina.

The tube posterior to the junction of the vagina and the urethra is the **urogenital** sinus and the opening to the exterior the **urogenital orifice**.

You are finished with your pig. Kiss her goodbye.

3. MALE GENITAL SYSTEM

Place a probe between the urinary bladder and the flap of the abdominal wall which still has the umbilical cord attached to it. Free the ventral surfce of the bladder from the abdominal wall flap by tearing the membrane. Using your scissors, cut across the wall flap between the male urogenital opening and the stump of the umbilical cord. Place the bladder in the body cavity so that it rests against the visceral organs. The sheath of the **penis** lies just below the skin in the ventral midline posterior to urogenital opening. Locate it by pressing the midline of the abdominal wall flap between your fingers. Using your scissors, expose the penis sheath by cutting through the skin. Continue cutting posteriorly until the penis sheath is exposed all the way to the posterior end of the body. Free the sheath from the surrounding tissue and cut through the wall flap just posterior to the urogenital opening and dorsal to the penis sheath. Place the penis sheath between the hind limbs of the pig so that it extends posterior to end of body. You can now remove the remains of the flap.

As in the female, in order to expose the **urethra**, the **pelvic girdle** must be cut. Place the point of the scissors into the opening into which the urethra disappears and cut through the pelvic girdle. Continue your cut posteriorly through the body wall to the point at which the penis sheath enters the body. Spread the hindlimbs by tightening the cords. Clear the tissue from around the urethra with your forceps.

You should be able to trace the urethra from the base of the bladder to the urogenital opening. Just before the urethra recurves anteriorly, locate two oval structures, the **bulbo-urethral** glands which lie on the dorsal surface of the urethra. In sexually mature animals, these glands produce the fluid in which the sperm are suspended, the **seminal fluid.**

The **testes** of the fetus are originally formed within the body cavity. During fetal development, they descend and are eventually located in two out-pocketings of the body wall, the **scrotal sacs.** The canal connecting the scrotal sacs and the body cavity is called the **inguinal canal.**

In a very young specimen, the testes may still be located within the body cavity. In older specimens, the testes will be partially or fully descended.

Locate the place at which the two **sperm ducts** join and enter the urethra on the dorsal surface of the urethra just posterior to the end of the bladder. Just posterior to this junction, locate the two **seminal vesicles,** which are another source of seminal fluid, along with the **prostate gland,** which is poorly developed in these fetal males.

Trace one of the sperm ducts to the point at which it disappears into the body wall. This is the entrance of the **inguinal canal.** Insert the point of your scissors into the inguinal canal and cut through the body wall so as to trace the path of the sperm duct into the scrotal sac. Within the scrotal sac, the sperm duct leads to the oval, brown **testis.** At this point, kiss your pig goodbye: he has given you his all.

After completing your dissection and observing your partner's, label all the major structures of the urogenital system on Figure 33.

4. HUMAN REPRODUCTIVE SYSTEMS

Examine the three-dimensional models of the human male and female reproductive systems. Be sure you understand the details of the anatomy of both sexes in relation to functions: sperm production and delivery in the male, and egg production and gestation (pregnancy) in the female.

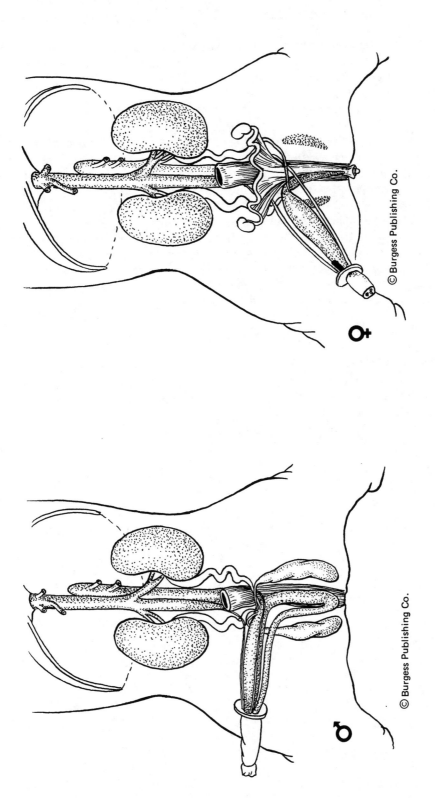

Figure 33 FETAL PIG, UROGENITAL ORGANS, MALE AND FEMALE

22

Reproduction:
Gametogenesis and Hormonal Regulation

INTRODUCTION

Gametogenesis may be defined as the process of formation and maturation ("ripening") of the gametes; that of the sperm is called **spermatogenesis** and that of the egg, **oogenesis.**

During the early embryonic existence of the animal, a comparatively small group of cells is set apart from the other cells and tissues. These cells from which gametes will arise are known as **primordial germ cells.**

The germ cells subsequently become enclosed in the gonads where they usually form sheets of cells, termed the **germinal epithelium,** which line the cavities within the gonads. In this condition they remain quiescent and comparatively undifferentiated for a time, sometimes for a considerable number of years, until the animal becomes sexually mature. Then these cells become active and form the gametes.

The <u>formation</u> of the gametes involves a special nuclear division called **meiosis.** This results in a reduction of the chromosome number from the **2N diploid** state to the **N haploid** state. Diploidy is re-established at **fertilization,** when the haploid sperm nucleus fuses with the haploid egg nucleus, resulting in a **zygote.**

The maturation of the gametes consists of cytoplasmic changes. In the testes, this results in a motile cell, the **sperm.** In the ovaries, the mature **egg** is a much larger cell which contains nutrients and other substances needed for the early divisions of the zygote.

The maturation of the gametes is under the control of hormones produced by the gonads and by the **pituitary gland.** The mechanism of hormonal control was studied in Exercise 18. The hormones specifically concerned with reproduction will be considered in this chapter. The male sex hormones, the **androgens,** not only regulate sperm production, but are also responsible for the male secondary sex characteristics, such as beard growth, muscular development and a low pitched voice.

The female sex hormones, primarily **estrogen** and **progesterone,** regulate the process of egg maturation and release, and the preparation of the uterus for pregnancy. Their presence accounts for female traits such as breast development and fat deposition in the area of the hips.

LABORATORY EXERCISES

PURPOSE

1) Prepared slides of the mammalian testis and ovary will be studied so that gametogenesis is understood.

2) Hormonal regulation and the ovarian and uterine cycles are presented. The emphasis is on an understanding of human sexual function.

1.   THE MAMMALIAN TESTIS AND SPERMATOGENESIS

Observe the prepared slide of the mouse testis, which is a cross-section of the entire structure. First look at the testis under the lowest magnification. Note the **epididymis** on one side which is composed of tubes containing maturing and mature sperm. The bulk of the testis consists of **seminiferous tubules** where spermatogenesis occurs. Focus on <u>one</u> tubule where, in section, the stages of this process may be seen (Figure 34). From the outer rim, and going successively toward the hollow center, look for **spermatogonia** (plural; singular = **spermatogonium**), **spermatocytes, spermatid** and **sperm**. These cell types correspond to the **meiotic stages**. Spermatogonia are **diploid** and spermatids are **haploid**. Note that the two meiotic divisions result in four spermatids from each spermatogonium. The spermatids **mature** into sperm, with a specialized structure for motility, the **flagellum**. There is modification of the cell body into a **head**, with a tip called the **acrosome**, containing special enzymes which aid in penetrating the egg and a midpiece, containing **mitochondria**.

Observe the demonstration slide of human sperm. Compare their appearance to the sperm seen in the inside of the seminiferous tubules of the mouse testis.

Other cells within the testis, the **interstitial cells** produce male sex hormones such as **testosterone**. The activity of these cells is regulated by the pituitary hormone **ICSH** (interstitial cell stimulating hormone). Another pituitary hormone **FSH** (follicle stimulating hormone) stimulates spermatogenesis.

2.   THE MAMMALIAN OVARY—DEVELOPING FOLLICLES

Obtain a prepared slide of an ovary.

Observe the entire ovary under the lowest magnification. Distributed near the outer area are a number of structures of varied sizes. These are the developing **follicles**. The **ovarian follicle** is a spherical structure within which the egg (**ovum**) develops. A **primary** follicle consists of a single layer of cells surrounding a slightly larger cell, the **primary oocyte**. The oocyte undergoes meiosis, and due to **unequal** cytoplasmic divisions, will give rise to <u>one</u> haploid egg. The follicle grows, becomes hollow and filled with fluid. The egg comes to lie on one side of the cavity surrounded by several layers of cells. Locate a follicle which shows the cavity, the egg, and the surrounding cells. Make a <u>clearly</u> <u>labelled</u> diagram.

Ovulation is the release of the egg from the follicle, which ruptures and discharges the egg into the abdominal cavity. It is picked up by the ciliary beat of the finger-like entrance of the **Fallopian tube**. It then passes down the Fallopian tube where the union of sperm and egg, or **fertilization**, occurs.

3.   CROSS-SECTION OF MAMMALIAN OVARY—SHOWING CORPUS LUTEUM

The follicle, as soon as it discharges the egg, begins to undergo important changes. The follicular cells grow and multiply, filling the cavity from which the egg was discharged and enlarging the entire structure, which is now called a **corpus luteum**. Its cells are usually stained pink in your slides. Locate a corpus luteum.

4.   THE OVARIAN CYCLE AND UTERINE CYCLES

Carefully review the wall charts detailing the hormonal changes of the female reproductive system.

The follicle and the corpus luteum function as endocrine glands, each secreting a specific hormone. That of the follicle is termed **estrogen**. It stimulates the thickening of the wall of the uterus, the **endometrium**, thus preparing it for the reception of the

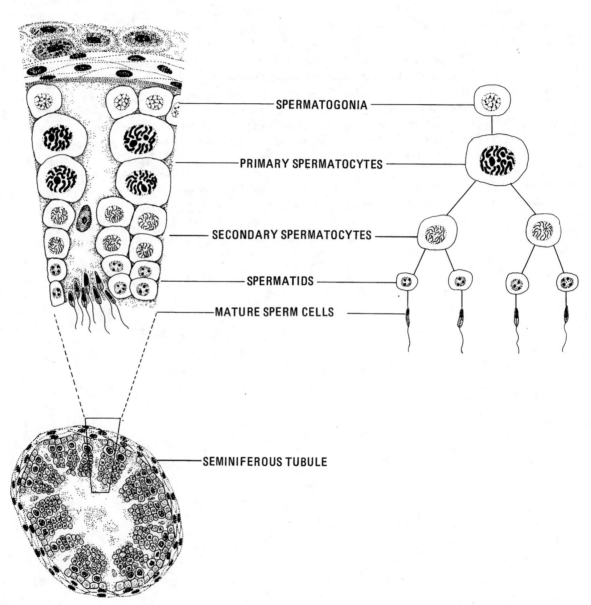

SPERMATOGONIA

PRIMARY SPERMATOCYTES

SECONDARY SPERMATOCYTES

SPERMATIDS

MATURE SPERM CELLS

SEMINIFEROUS TUBULE

Figure 34 SPERMATOGENESIS

zygote. After the follicle breaks, less estrogen is formed; but the developing corpus luteum then produces its characteristic hormone, **progesterone.** Progesterone continues the stimulation of the uterus, causing its wall to thicken and develop a rich system of blood vessels. These changes specifically prepare the uterus for the pregnancy which may follow.

The corpus luteum develops under stimulation from the pituitary hormone, **LH,** luteinizing hormone. If, however, the egg is not fertilized and does not implant in the uterine wall, the corpus luteum degenerates. The wall itself stops growing and, in the primates, is sloughed off with a discharge of blood. This process is known as **menstruation.**

Meantime, in the ovary one or more new follicles, each containing an egg, have begun to enlarge so that, in time, the above cycle will be repeated. The enlargement is stimulated by **FSH,** follicle stimulating hormone, from the pituitary.

The cyclic nature of the ovarian and uterine changes is due to the changes in the levels of the hormones produced by the ovary and by the pituitary gland. There is a system of **feedback control** (already discussed in Exercise 18) which accounts for follicle growth followed by corpus luteum growth.

The understanding of the physiology of reproduction and the anatomy of the reproductive tract has led to advances in controlling the process of reproduction. These include the birth control pills and operations such as a vasectomy. Review, once more, both the models of the human male and female reproductive systems and the hormonal regulation of the female reproductive system in terms of human sexual function.

23

Development

INTRODUCTION

The fertilized egg, the **zygote**, contains all the genetic information necessary for the development of the complete organism. There are two aspects to development. The first, **growth**, is due to an increase in cell number accomplished by cellular division. The process of **mitosis** results in all the cells receiving the same information. The second, **differentiation**, is the formation of different cell types, tissues, organ and organ systems. It is not completely understood how this diversity of type is superimposed upon genetic identity. It is known that the structures formed early in embryonic development are involved in cellular determination.

The initial stages of development, the **embryonic stages**, are similar in most organisms. In related organisms, such as the vertebrates (fishes, amphibians, reptiles, birds, and mammals), the very early stages are nearly indistinguishable. The embryo is surrounded by protective **membranes**. In fishes and amphibians, embryonic development occurs in water, with wastes diffusing, and gas exchange occurring across the protective membranes. Nutrients come from the yolk present in the egg. In birds and reptiles, a shelled, **land egg** evolved. An external watery environment is no longer necessary for embryonic development and the embryonic membranes store the yolk and receive wastes. The shell allows for gas diffusion. In placental mammals the embryo and its membranes develop inside the **uterus**. A specialized structure, the **placenta**, is formed from embryonic and maternal tissue. It is the place where nutrient, gas and waste exchange occurs between the mother and the embryo. After the second month, the human embryo is called the fetus.

LABORATORY EXERCISES

PURPOSE

1) The early embryonic stages are studied with an emphasis on the relation between initial cellular organization and later development of organ systems.

2) The course of human embryonic and fetal development is illustrated.

1. SLIDES OF DEVELOPMENT OF SEA URCHIN AND STARFISH

Sea urchins and starfishes are Echinoderms, invertebrate marine organisms. They are used because of the availability of the material and the ease of preparation of slides. In addition, in Echinoderms, the planes of the initial cleavage divisions of the organisms are the same as those of the vertebrates.

Eggs were fertilized in dishes of sea water and at various stages in development were preserved and stained. Several of each stage were mounted whole on the slide, so that the preparation is quite thick. Study under low and medium powers. Do not use high power. Look for each of the following **stages of early development**. (Figures 35 and 36).

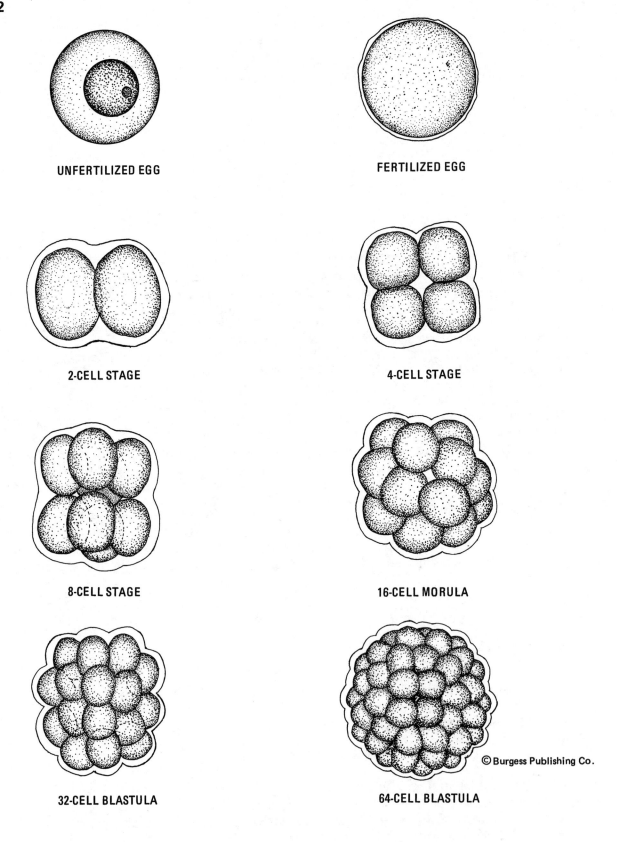

UNFERTILIZED EGG

FERTILIZED EGG

2-CELL STAGE

4-CELL STAGE

8-CELL STAGE

16-CELL MORULA

32-CELL BLASTULA

64-CELL BLASTULA

© Burgess Publishing Co.

Figure 35 ONTOGENY OF ECHINODERM THROUGH BLASTULA

133

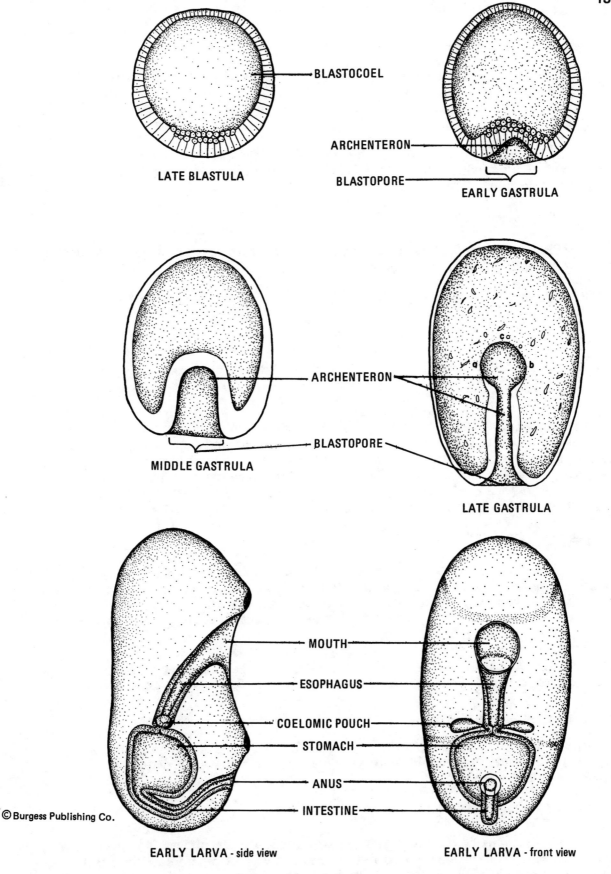

Figure 36 ONTOGENY OF ECHINODERM, LATE BLASTULA TO LARVA

A. Unfertilized Egg

This spherical structure is recognizable by its large clear nucleus with a denser solid nucleolus.

B. Zygote

In the fertilized egg, or zygote, the nucleus is indistinct. With appropriate adjustment of illumination, the **fertilization membrane** may readily be seen as an irregular surrounding film.

C. Two Blastomere Stage

The first cleavage division of the zygote results in formation of two blastomeres within the fertilization membrane.

D. Four Blastomere Stage

and

E. Eight Blastomere Stage

Note that each blastomere (cell) is progressively smaller as cleavage continues.

F. Morula to Blastula

Successive cleavages double the number of cells: 16, 32, 64, and so on. However, since the protoplasm is liquid, the cells tend to round out and a space appears in the middle of the group. As the number of cells increases, the central space enlarges until the embryo is seen to consist of a single layer of cells around a central cavity. This stage is the **blastula** and the cavity is called the **blastocoel.** The blastula is able to swim. The embryo has not increased in size.

G. Gastrulation

Continued cell division causes **invagination,** or ingrowth, of cells at one pole of the embryo. This inner layer of cells is called the **endoderm** or inner germ layer. The early gastrula is characterized by a pouch of **endoderm** cells invading the blastocoel. The cells that remain on the outside constitute the **ectoderm** or outer germ layer. From now on, all stages are free swimming.

Invagination continues and in the **late gastrula** the tube of endoderm extends almost to the opposite pole. The cavity of the tube is the **archenteron,** or developing digestive tract, and its opening to the outside, the **blastopore,** later becomes the **anus.**

H. Mesoderm Formation

From the inner end of the **archenteron,** pouches grow laterally into the blastocoel and form the **mesoderm,** or middle germ layer. When the nervous system develops, the embryo is called a neurula.

I. Larval Stages

The significance of the three germ layers, endoderm, mesoderm and ectoderm is that later organ systems can be shown to have originated from one of these layers. Thus, the nervous system and the skin derive from ectoderm, muscle and bone from mesoderm, and as already seen, the digestive tract from endoderm.

As structures become visible, the developing organism is called a **larva**. On the slide, look for early larval stages in which the digestive tract can be seen from mouth to anus.

Review all the stages you have seen on the slide and compare them to the three-dimensional models of early cleavage and gastrulation and to Figures 35 and 36.

2. MAMMALIAN DEVELOPMENT

A. Demonstration Of Pig Uterus

Observe the preserved uterus of a mature pig, containing embryos. Compare the size of this uterus with the structure you saw in the fetal pig. Compare the size of these embryos, and their developmental state, to the fetal pig you dissected. Look for the attachment of the **umbilical** cord to the **placenta**.

The mammalian embryo is surrounded by several membranes. The outermost, the **chorion**, contributes to the placenta. The innermost, the **amnion**, protects the fetus, which is floating in **amniotic fluid**. Look for these two membranes.

B. Demonstration of Preserved Mammalian Embryos

Compare the pig and human embryo at different developmental levels. Note the similarities in the early stages. Observe the various charts and models showing the developing human fetus within the uterus. At the time of birth, contractions of the uterine muscles force the fetus out of the uterus, into the vagina, and out into its new world.

24

Genetics

INTRODUCTION

Genetics is the science of heredity. All living organisms manifest a great deal of **variability,** or differences in their characteristics. Some of these **traits** are inherited from one generation to the next. At other times new traits seem to appear in offspring which were not manifested in the parents. There are certain basic principles which apply to the inheritance of traits. These were proposed by **Gregor Mendel** who deduced them from experiments with garden peas. He worked with several well-defined contrasting pairs of characteristics which are now called **phenotypes.** Two of the contrasting pairs he worked with were round or wrinkled seeds and long or short stems.

Mendel first obtained pure (true-breeding) lines of each of these contrasting characters, then followed the inheritance of single character pairs independently of the others. He found that when he crossed **parents (P_1)** differing in one contrasting pair, only one of the characters appeared in the **first filial generation (F_1).** Yet when plants of the F_1 generation were crossed, the contrasting character which had disappeared in the F_1 reappeared in the **second filial (F_2)** generation, in the ratio of **three** plants with the character evident in F_1 **to one** plant with the character which had disappeared in the F_1.

To explain this, Mendel postulated that each germ cell (gamete) carried a factor for only one of the contrasting characters, and that in the F_1 the factors for the contrasting characters existed together, with one dominating the other, so that all of the individuals had the appearance of the dominating character. But in the formation of the germ cells by the F_1, the factors of the contrasting pair were separated or **segregated,** with each germ cell again getting only one factor but not both. This discovery is now known as Mendel's first law, or the **law of segregation**—that is, segregation of the factors controlling a character.

Mendel next studied the inheritance of two contrasting character pairs considered together, and found that the results could be explained by assuming that the factors for the two different characters assorted independently of one another in the formation of the germ cells, and then recombined in all possible combinations in the formation of the F_2. This has become known as Mendel's second law, or the **law of independent assortment.**

Mendel's factors are called **alleles** and are known to be found on specific places, **gene loci** (singular, locus) on the chromosomes. The particular alleles present in an organism define its **genotype.**

LABORATORY EXERCISES

PURPOSE

In this exercise, we will study Mendel's laws, using only one or two traits. Keep in mind that the final phenotype of any organism is due to an array of factors: Genetic, developmental, and environmental. As part of the exercise, environmental influences on phenotype will be considered.

1. CORN EARS

Mendel derived his laws mathematically, based on the **phenotype ratios** in the F_2 generation. Each seed on an ear of corn represents a separate organism (actually the embryo and its food or endosperm), and the large number of seeds per ear should result in a good approximation of the expected ratios. The F_2 ears you are to examine are lacquered and have two sets of contrasting phenotypes.

A cross where the parents differ in two gene pairs is a **dihybrid cross** (Figure 37). The phenotypes are the color of the seed and the amount of sugar in the endosperm. The dominant allele $\underline{R}$ controls the production of the purple pigment, anthocyanin. If the genotype is $\underline{rr}$, the seed is yellow or white. Starchy is the dominant condition in the endosperm. The recessive genotype $\underline{su/su}$ results in seeds high in sugar. When the corn is dry, sweet seeds are wrinkled and starchy seeds are smooth.

A. The Law of Segregation

The law of segregation, which predicts a 3:1 ratio in the F_2, can be observed by scoring one of the contrasting phenotypes, color. Choose one row at random on the ear of corn. Count all the purple seeds in this row, record the number, then count all the yellow seeds. Repeat for the four rows adjacent to this first row and record the total number of purple seeds and yellow seeds:

	PURPLE	YELLOW	TOTAL
observed			
expected	(3/4)	(1/4)	(4/4)

Calculate the expected number on the basis of 3/4 purple: 1/4 yellow seeds and compare the expected and observed.

B. The Law of Independent Assortment

Choose another five rows on the preserved ear of corn and now score each seed for both phenotypes as indicated (remember the smooth appearance indicates a high starch content). Calculate the expected numbers of each phenotype.

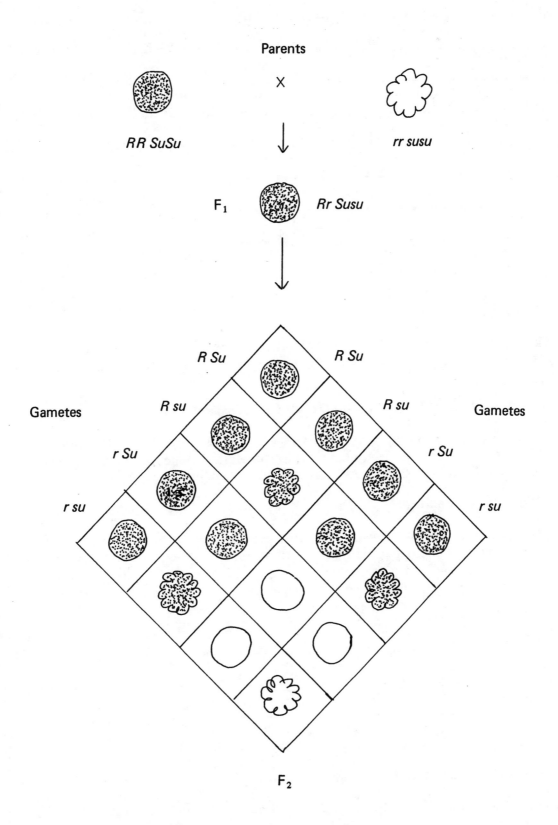

Figure 37 THE DIHYBRID CROSS

	PURPLE STARCHY	PURPLE SWEET	YELLOW STARCHY	YELLOW SWEET	TOTAL
observed on 5 rows					
expected	9/16	3/16	3/16	1/16	16/16

Finally, from the above data, add columns 1+3 for the total number of starchy seeds, and column 2+4 for the number of sweet seeds. What is the ratio of starchy to sweet _____?

2. CORN SEEDLINGS: THE ROLE OF THE ENVIRONMENT

The corn seedlings in the laboratory represent the F_2 of a **monohybrid** cross, involving one set of contrasting phenotypes. The albino phenotype is due to a recessive allele, and is **lethal**. The green seedlings contain chlorophyll.

A. Light-Grown Seedlings

Observe the colors on these plants. How closely does the content of a single planter approximate the expected F_2 phenotypic ratio? Tabulate the class total:

	GREEN	ALBINO	TOTAL
observed			
expected			

B.   Dark-Grown Seedlings

Observe the color on these plants. Can you tell which are albinos? What happens to plants grown in the dark? These plants will now be exposed to light. Be sure to observe them at the next laboratory period. What are the necessary components for the synthesis of chlorophyll in the corn seedling?

DEMONSTRATIONS

Observe the corn mounts and charts. Note the great variability. Although it is not possible to have many different organisms in the lab, it is important to remember that all living things are subject to the laws of inheritance.

25

Human Genetics

INTRODUCTION

As noted in the previous Exercise, the laws of inheritance apply to all living things, including human beings. However, it is neither practical nor ethical to do genetic experiments on humans. Nevertheless, a great deal is known about human genetics, primarily from **pedigree** studies, which trace the inheritance of traits in existing families. Recent advances in **cytogenetics** (the study of chromosomes) and other specialized areas, such as **immunogenetics**, have increased our understanding of both normal and abnormal phenotypes. Genetic diseases, disorders due to the presence of certain genes or chromosomes in the affected individual, can now be diagnosed early, often before birth. The more we understand the genetic bases of disease, the closer we come to treatment or prevention of these diseases.

The total phenotype which comprises the individual, is the result of the potential determined by the genotype developing in a particular environment. As a result of genetic variability and diverse individual experience, each person is unique.

LABORATORY EXERCISES

PURPOSE

This exercise will demonstrate some human phenotypes and genotypes, and the great variability found in human beings.

1. HUMAN PHENOTYPES

Some phenotypes, such as the shape of the nose, or the color of the skin, indicate the range of possible phenotypic expression possible. Their inheritance is complicated by multiple genes and environmental effects. Other phenotypes are characterized by simple alternative manifestations and it is possible to classify people as being either one or the other. Such alternative phenotypes are usually due to alternative alleles at a single gene locus. This exercise will consist of determining the phenotype and where possible, the genotype, for several common traits. If the trait is due to a recessive allele, and you show this trait, the genotype is **homozygous**, that is both alleles are the same. Thus, the genotype would be written aa. If the trait is due to a dominant allele, you may be either homozygous, with both dominant alleles, or **heterozygous**, that is have one dominant and one recessive allele. In such cases the genotype is written A—. Record your phenotype and genotype for the following traits on page 147. Some of these phenotypes are illustrated in Figure 38.

144

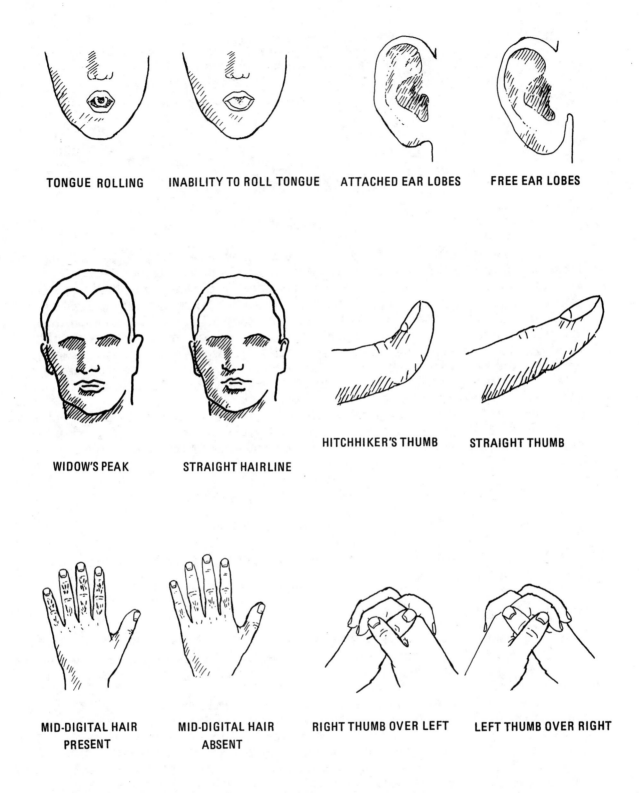

TONGUE ROLLING   INABILITY TO ROLL TONGUE   ATTACHED EAR LOBES   FREE EAR LOBES

WIDOW'S PEAK   STRAIGHT HAIRLINE   HITCHHIKER'S THUMB   STRAIGHT THUMB

MID-DIGITAL HAIR PRESENT   MID-DIGITAL HAIR ABSENT   RIGHT THUMB OVER LEFT   LEFT THUMB OVER RIGHT

Figure 38 HUMAN GENETIC TRAITS CONTROLLED BY SINGLE GENES

A. Attached Ear Lobes

Some people have the ears attached directly to the head so that no lobe hangs free. If you have tried to wear clip-on earrings and have lost them, you probably have attached ear lobes. The lobe hanging free is due to a dominant allele E.

B. Tongue Rolling

This favorite trait of geneticists may actually not be due to a single dominant gene, R, but it is still possible to divide people into those who can roll their tongue into a trough when the tongue is stuck out from the mouth and those whose tongue remains flattened.

C. PTC Tasting

This is a close runner-up to tongue rolling as a trait used to divide the population into those who can, and those who cannot. This time, it is the ability to taste Phenylthiocarbamide (PTC). Tasters have the dominant allele T and can taste this harmless chemical. It may be that tasters may find either more or less attractive certain foods such as spinach or turnips. Nontasters will not react to the PTC test, but of course can taste other substances.

First place the control strip in your mouth (do not chew) to get the paper taste. Then place the PTC paper in your mouth and allow at least 10 seconds (again do not chew the paper) for your saliva to dissolve the PTC. You will know if you are a taster!

D. Widow's Peak

The hairline can be either straight across, or drop down to a point. The point is known as widow's peak and is due to a dominant gene, W. If you have hair, pull it straight back from your forehead to determine your phenotype.

E. Hitchhiker's Thumb

Try bending your right thumb back as shown in Figure 38. If you succeed, you have hyperextensibility due to a recessive allele h. Some people will be able to dramatically flex this joint backwards. If the thumb remains straight, try the left thumb. Occasionally only one thumb shows this trait.

F. Mid-digital Hair

Look for the presence of hair on the middle joint of your fingers. Look on all four fingers of each hand carefully. The presence of hair on at least one middle joint is due to a dominant allele M. Note that there may be **variable expression** of this trait, in terms of which fingers and how many have hair.

G. Thumb Over

Quickly clasp your hands together, interlocking the fingers. Observe whether your left thumb is over the right or vice versa (Figure 38). The left thumb on top appears to be due to a dominant gene F, and the right thumb on top is the recessive condition.

146

H.   Iris Pigmentation

The color of the eye is determined by the amount of pigment (melanin) present in the iris. There is one gene which determines whether or not pigment will be deposited. If the dominant allele P is present, the eye will be of varying shades, depending on other genes. Blue (or sometimes grey) eyes result when no pigment is present to mask the blue (or grey) layer in the back of the iris. This is the recessive condition.

I.   Index Finger Length

Some people have the second (index) longer than the fourth (ring) finger, while in others the ring finger is longer. Determine your phenotype as follows. Put your right hand on the page so that the end of your fourth finger (excluding nail overhang) is on the line. Your fingers must be parallel to the page edge. Draw a line at the tip of your second finger.

second finger mark: fourth finger tip on this line:

_____

If the mark is on or above the line, the second finger is longer; below the line, shorter. Tabulate the class data according to sex. This is a **sex-influenced** trait: Male heterozygotes will have a shorter index finger while female heterozygotes will have the longer finger.

J.   Blood Type

The surface of the red blood cells has many antigenic proteins. We will look at two gene loci controlling these proteins. The ABO series is under the control of gene I. The A-antigen allele is I^A; the B-antigen allele is I^B; the recessive phenotype, O, means neither A nor B antigen is present and the genotype is ii. I^A and I^B are **codominant**. Note that unlike the other traits observed, there are more than two alleles at this gene locus. The ABO system is an example of **multiple alleles.**

The second gene locus, Rh, is more complex. For the purposes of this exercise, we can designate the presence of the Rh antigen as due to the dominant allele D. A person's ABO phenotype is determined independently of the Rh phenotype. The genes

	RECORD YOUR PHENOTYPE	GIVE YOUR GENOTYPE	NUMBER OF EACH IN THE CLASS
ear lobes			attached:
			free:
tongue rolling			can:
			cannot:
PTC tasting			yes:
			no:
widow's peak			present:
			absent:
hitchhiker's thumb			present:
			absent:
mid–digital hair			present:
			absent:
thumb over			left top:
			right top:
iris pigmentation			pigmented:
			blue:
index finger length			male longer:
			female longer:
			male shorter:
			female shorter:
blood type			O:
record (+) or (−) for RH			A:
			B:
			AB:

for these two traits are separate. An understanding of the inheritance of these and other cell-surface antigens is important in medical genetics, especially in blood transfusions and tissue transplantation.

We will score for the presence of the A and B antigens and the Rh (D) antigen. If any of these antigens are present, your blood cells will agglutinate (clump) in the presence of a specific antibody. The sera are color-coded to help you determine your blood type.

AGGLUTINATION IN

Blood Type	anti-A (blue)	anti-B (yellow)	anti-Rh (colorless)
O-	-	-	-
O+	-	-	+
A-	+	-	-
A+	+	-	+
B-	-	+	-
B+	-	+	+
AB-	+	+	-
AB+	+	+	+

2. HUMAN VARIABILITY

We can use the class trait tabulation to demonstrate the genetic individuality of the class members. With the exception of identical (**monozygotic**) twins, each person should be genetically unique.

Calculate the frequency of each phenotype. For example, 2/20 student (.10) may have attached ear lobes and 10/20 (.50) may be type 0. Since these two are independently determined phenotypes, the odds of someone being both type 0 and having attached lobes, would be .10 x .50 or .05. This means that one student in the class would have both these phenotypes. On this basis it is possible that several students may share two, three, or four traits, but is is unlikely that any two students in the class will be alike for all the traits tested.

Compare your phenotypes with the person sitting next to you as follows: In order, determine how many phenotypes you have in common before you become different. For example, you may both have free ear lobes and tongue rolling ability, but only one of you is a taster. Thus, you have two common phenotypes before you diverge (ignore the others). Two others may not diverge until hitchhiker's thumb, and would have four common phenotypes. Determine the average number of traits to divergence for the class. Remember, we are considering very few traits and that there are about 100,000 human genes.

26

Evolution

INTRODUCTION

Evolution is the unifying concept of biology. Evolution means <u>change</u>, and more particularly, change over <u>time</u>. Biological evolution is the change in organisms leading ultimately to new adaptations and to diversity. The principle of natural selection was proposed by Charles Darwin and Alfred Wallace to explain the origin of new species (groups of similar interbreeding organisms). Natural selection depends on the existence of genetic variability. Those variants which are best adapted to a particular environment will be the most likely to survive and reproduce. This differential reproductive success, coupled with other mechanisms such as reproductive or geographic isolation, ultimately leads to new species. Implicit in this is that there will be similarities among species. Many of the exercises in this manual, designed to help us know more about ourselves, are based on the universality of basic life processes in all living organisms. Thus, we looked at mitosis in onion cells and cleavage in sea urchins. The similarities between all mammals enabled us to use the dissection of the fetal pig to understand human anatomy. Comparative anatomy and other comparative studies of biochemical, chromosomal, and developmental characteristics are powerful tools for determining the nature and direction of evolutionary changes. The fossil record indicates what ancestral species were like and when they existed. The fossil record also shows that some species died out (extinction) and others are very stable.

Evolutionary changes in some cases require millions of years and cannot be directly observed. Some variations, such as antibiotic resistance in bacterial strains, are more rapidly established.

LABORATORY EXERCISES

PURPOSE

We will study evolution by: (1) doing an exercise in the comparative anatomy of the vertebrate skeleton and (2) observing examples of fossil hominid skulls.

1. THE VERTEBRATE SKELETON

The vertebrates are the fishes, amphibians, reptiles, birds, and mammals. The skeleton consists of the axial skeleton, which includes the skull, vertebral column, ribs and sternum (breast-bone) and the appendicular skeleton, which includes the pectoral (shoulder) girdle, the pelvic (hip) girdle, and the appendages (limbs). We will see examples of **homology**, where these parts, of common origin, have changed over evolutionary time for different functions. Thus, homologous structures, in spite of their biological relatedness, may have different appearances and functions, whereas **analogous** structures will have similar functions but will have evolved from biologically unrelated components.

A. The Axial Skeleton

  1) Skull: All vertebrate skulls have similar bones, but differences in number, shape and proportions of these components make for a wide variety of appearances, such as you see in the samples around the laboratory. Examine the teeth of the mammalian species to see the adaptive modifications for different diets.

  2) Vertebral Column: Note that the human backbone is made up of a series of individual bones, the vertebrae, each of which can move slightly with respect to its neighbor in the vertebral column. In four-legged animals it is easier to see in side view that the series of vertebrae form, in effect, a supporting girder which stiffens the body and prevents it from sagging between the pectoral and pelvic girdles, which themselves are supported by the legs. The vertebral column also protects the spinal cord of the nervous system from injury.
  Examine the cat skeleton and the frog skeleton mount. While studying the parts, try to see the fitness of the structures (adaptation) for the functions they carry out.

  3) Ribs and Sternum: In the thoracic region the rib basket (ribs and sternum) gives added support to the body wall. In humans and other mammals the movement of the ribs functions also in respiration.

Compare the sternum of any mammal with that of a bird. What structural feature of the bird sternum is different from any of the mammal skeletons in the laboratory?

For what function is this feature an adaptation in birds?

B. The Appendicular Skeleton

  1) Pectoral Girdle: On the frog skeleton, note that the upper bone of the foreleg is attached to the axial skeleton by means of three bones which almost encircle the body at that anterior-posterior level. Connecting the shoulder joint to the sternum ventrally, note two bones, the anterior clavicle and the posterior coracoid. From the shoulder joint dorsally, note the scapula (shoulder blade). Muscles and tendons attach the scapula to the spinous processes of the vertebrae, thus anchoring the pectoral girdle to the axial skeleton dorsally. These three elements appear in the pectoral girdle of all vertebrates, but their arrangement is adapted for the direction and variety of movement the forelimbs carry out in locomotion. Notice that in primates adapted for climbing trees (study the monkey skeleton) there are only two bones in the pectoral girdle, the clavicle and the scapula. The coracoid is no longer a separate bone connecting with the sternum, but can be seen as the small coracoid process completely fused with the scapula near the shoulder joint. What is the extent of the coracoid bone in the human skeleton?

  2) Pelvic Girdle: The posterior limb is also attached to the axial skeleton by means of a girdle consisting of three bones. These three are fused into a single pelvis, the hipbone.

  Note the differences in the pelvic girdle in an aquatic skeleton (fish), a tetrapod terrestial skeleton (cat), and a bipedal terrestial skeleton (human).

3) <u>Appendages:</u>

a) Components of the limbs: Both pairs of appendages have a similar basic plan of structure and show, therefore, the principle of homology.

b) Adaptive modification among forelimbs: All four-legged vertebrates have inherited the same basic plan of forelimb structure. Different species build out of this basic plan a forelimb that can do different things. Some can swim (seal, porpoise); some can fly (birds, bats); some can run on hard ground (horses); some can walk on their hind legs, thus freeing their forelegs for other uses (birds, kangaroos, man); some can dig below the ground (moles); and some can climb trees (apes, monkeys). In each case the structure is adapted to fit the kind of movement needed for locomotion in the particular environment.

Animals adapted primarily for swimming exert their power in locomotion more through movements of the vertebral column than through movements of the forelimb. The relative involvement of forelimb and backbone in animals adapted primarily for flying or climbing can be determined as follows:

Measure the length of the vertebral column and the forelimb of the skeletons of the fish, lizard, bird, bat and monkey. Does the ratio of length of forelimb (including digits) to length of vertebral column (including tail) for the following animals fit in with your expectations?

APPENDAGE AND AXIS LENGTH

	FISH	LIZARD	PIGEON	BAT	MONKEY
A. Forelimb plus digits					
B. Spine plus tail					
C. Ratio A/B					

Animals which show less adaptive modification on their limb structure (i.e., are not so specialized for particular modes of locomotion) can do a variety of things. A cat, for instance, can not only walk, but can also swim and climb. Where would you expect the apendage-axis measurements of the cat to fit in your table above? Examine a cat and record the figures.

Compare the human arm with the arm of a monkey. List in adjacent columns as many points of similarity and points of difference as you can observe.

The human arm is no longer used primarily for locomotion. For what type of locomotion do you think it shows adaptation?

What do you conclude from comparing the human arm with other vertebrate forelimbs seen in the laboratory about the locomotor habits of prehuman ancestors?

2. HUMAN EVOLUTION

A. Introduction

The evolutionary development of the human species is traced by a study of the fossil record. This consists of bones whose ages have been determined by radioactive isotope (Potassium/Argon ratios) dating and by geomagnetic (periodic predictable reversals of the earth's magnetic field) dating of the geological layers where the fossil bones are found. The key traits separating hominid (manlike) fossils from pongid (apelike) fossils are bipedalism (walking upright) and jaw shape and tooth size and, in later fossils, the larger cranial capacity. The structure of limb and pelvic bones allows conclusions to be made about the mode of locomotion. Markings on the teeth can be correlated with diet. Casts of the inside of the skull tell about brain development.

It is clear from the study of fossils that bipedalism evolved 3.5 million years ago. The extraordinary brain growth that led to the genus Homo occurred later. The oldest known modern human fossils are only 40,000 years old. Our species, Homo sapiens is a relative newcomer.

B. Fossil Skulls

A series of fossil skulls and head reconstructions are available in the laboratory. The skulls are plastic casts of the actual fossil finds, and are either incomplete or have filled-in areas of different colors representing the missing pieces. The heads are a representation of what these extinct pre-humans might have looked like if they had been completely preserved. Note particularly the changes in cranial capacity, reflecting increases in brain size. Tooth size is also a variable: molars got relatively smaller and front teeth relatively larger as Homo evolved.

1) Australopithecus (Zinjanthropus) head: This represents an extinct hominid line which preceded and then coexisted with the genus Homo, to which modern humans belong. The earliest of the Australopithecines (A. afarensis) was bipedal, had large molars and a small brain and existed 3.5 million years ago. This particular specimen was found in East Africa and is 1.8 million years old. Stone tools were found near these fossils.

2) Homo erectus (Sinanthropus) skull and head. This extinct species first appeared about 1.5 million years ago. While the cranium and jaw are primitive, the pelvic bones that were found are essentially modern. Brain size is increased. This particular specimen (Peking man) dates from one-half million years ago. Many flaked stone tools and evidence of fire use are found with these forms.

3) Steinheim skull and head. This specimen is named after its place of discovery and is about 200,000 years old. The teeth are smaller and modern in shape, but its relationship to the evolution of Homo is unclear.

4) Homo sapiens neanderthalensis skull and head. The shape of Neanderthal's skull is not quite modern, but the brain size is not significantly different from modern humans. This species is named after the Neander Valley in Germany, although fossils have been found in Asia, Africa and throughout Europe where this species existed 100,000 years ago. This is the first group known to bury its dead.

5)   <u>Cro-magnon</u> skull and head. <u>Homo</u> <u>sapiens</u> <u>sapiens</u>, the species contemporary humans belong to appeared 40,000 years ago. This skull is about 25,000 years old and represents what is colloquially referred to as "cave men." The Cro-magnon skull is less robust than the Neanderthal and the brain is slightly smaller. Many of the well known cave paintings were done by members of this group and bone needles and statuettes are also found among Cro-magnon artifacts.

6)   <u>Homo</u> <u>sapiens</u> <u>sapiens</u>, current. No significant changes in brain size, locomotion or anatomy have occurred compared to Cro-magnon. The main changes have been cultural, marked especially by the transition from hunting to farming about 10,000 years ago. Humans are still evolving, but the dramatic differences between Cro-magnon and modern <u>Homo</u> <u>sapiens</u> are due to cultural changes. These in turn ultimately depend on the results of bio-evolution, especially bipedalism, which freed the forelimbs and the highly developed cerebral cortex correlated with speech and language, which enables us to study ourselves.